Contents

About the Program

Strengthening Math Skills: Geometry Grades 1–2 can be used to introduce geometry concepts, review and enhance skills, practice skills, and apply key mathematics vocabulary. The program provides instruction and practice in the geometry skills recommended by the National Council of Teachers of Mathematics (NCTM), as well as additional standards necessary to meet various state curriculums. A correlation to the NCTM standards can be found on page 4 of this book.

Five units progress logically to build upon skills, utilize prior knowledge, apply skills and strategies, and make connections between mathematical concepts. For example, children learn to recognize shapes by their attributes, conduct activities to find shapes in the real world, sort shapes to compare how they are alike and different, and apply what they know about shapes to recognize plane shapes on the faces of solid figures. They also use what they know about shapes to make patterns, learn about position and movement, and learn about perimeter and area.

Getting Started

Level Assessment

A four-page Level Assessment is included on pages 5–8 to use as a Pretest or Posttest. It is organized into two sections so that it can be administered two pages at a time. Part A includes content that is taught and practiced in Units 1–3. Part B covers the content of Units 4 and 5. If needed, Part A can even be administered as a cumulative test after the first three units have been completed.

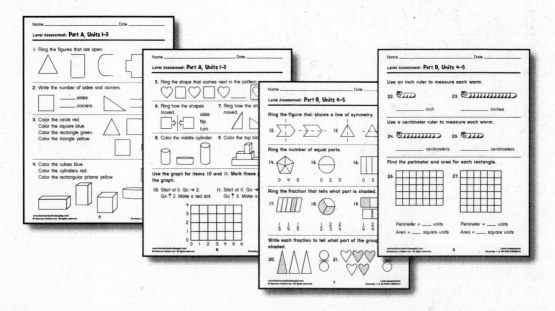

Manipulatives

Children will benefit from the use of hands-on manipulatives as they explore each lesson concept, make applications, and complete the activities. You might want to collect some of the following manipulatives for children to use throughout the program: attribute links and blocks, boxes, building blocks, cans, centimeter cubes, connecting cubes, fraction circles and strips, one-inch square tiles.

For activities that ask children to cut out plane shapes from art paper, you might want to cut several in advance. It would also be helpful to have grid paper or dot paper available for some of the units.

Meeting the Needs of All Learners

- Each vocabulary word is introduced in simple language and included in the Glossary at the end of the book. Children may benefit by sharing word translations in their native languages. Each vocabulary word is also boldfaced to make revisiting the definition and example easy to find.

- The two practice pages in each lesson provide different approaches to demonstrating an understanding of the lesson concepts. Some children may find that they are comfortable completing the first page independently but may find the second page more challenging.

- The activities are designed to be useful for children at all levels, allowing for various correct answers and depth of applications. Some of the activities may require that the teacher or parent read aloud the directions.

Unit Organization

- 5 units: Plane Figures, Solid Figures, Movement and Location, Equal Parts, and Measurement
- 5 lessons in each unit
- 1-page Assessment for each unit
- 2 blackline masters for each unit, found in the back of the book

Lesson Organization

- 4 pages: Instruction, Practice, More Practice, Activities
- The first page of each lesson provides instruction in concepts and vocabulary.
- Two pages of practice provide more than one way to apply lesson concepts.
- The last page of each lesson provides hands-on applications of concepts. To complete these activities, children may be asked to use manipulatives, make games, use the blackline masters provided, explore their real world, draw or write to record their work, and communicate mathematically.

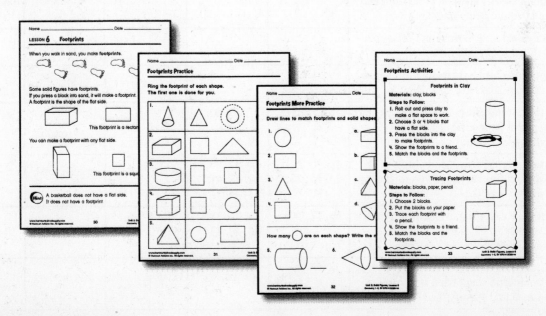

NCTM Standards Correlation

NCTM Standard	Unit 1 pages	Unit 2 pages	Unit 3 pages	Unit 4 pages	Unit 5 pages
2D and 3D Shapes: recognize, name, build, draw, compare, and sort two- and three-dimensional shapes	9–12, 13–16, 17–20, 21–24, 25–28	30–33, 34–37, 38–41, 42–45, 46–49	54, 57, 58		
2D and 3D Shapes: describe attributes and parts of two- and three-dimensional shapes	13–16, 17–20, 21–24	30–33, 34–37, 38–41, 42–45		72, 76–79, 80–83, 84–87	
2D and 3D Shapes: investigate and predict the results of putting together and taking apart two- and three-dimensional shapes	12, 20	36, 37, 41, 45	55–58		
Spatial Relationships: describe, name, and interpret relative positions in space and apply ideas about relative position			51–54, 59–62, 63, 65, 66		
Spatial Relationships: describe, name, and interpret direction and distance in navigating space and apply ideas about direction and distance			62, 63, 65, 66		
Spatial Relationships: find and name locations with simple relationships such as "near to" and in coordinate systems such as maps			59–62, 63, 65, 66, 67–70		
Measurement: recognize the attributes of length, volume, weight, area, and time				93–96, 97–100, 101–104, 105–108, 109–112	
Measurement: compare and order objects according to their attributes				95–96, 99–100	
Measurement: understand how to measure using nonstandard and standard units				93–96, 97–100, 101–104, 108, 112	
Measurement: select an appropriate unit and tool for the attribute being measured				96, 100, 104, 108	
Transformations and Symmetry: recognize and apply slides, flips, and turns			51–54		
Transformations and Symmetry: recognize and create shapes that have symmetry				72–75, 79	
Visualization, Reasoning, Modeling: create mental images of geometric shapes using spatial memory and spatial visualization	16	31, 36, 40, 42, 43, 45, 49	58		
Visualization, Reasoning, Modeling: recognize and represent shapes from different perspectives	18–20, 22, 23, 25, 26	30–32, 35, 37, 38–41, 43–45	54, 55–58		
Visualization, Reasoning, Modeling: relate ideas in geometry to ideas in number and measurement	16, 17, 24	34, 36, 38, 40, 42, 43	58, 65, 66, 67–70	91	96, 100, 104, 108
Visualization, Reasoning, Modeling: recognize geometric shapes and structures in the environment and specify their location	28	37, 40, 41, 44	62		

Geometry 1–2, SV 9781419099144

Level Assessment: **Part A, Units 1-3**

1. Ring the figures that are open.

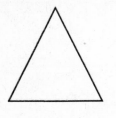 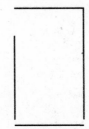  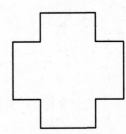

2. Write the number of sides and corners.

 _____ sides

_____ corners

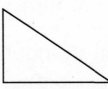 _____ sides

_____ corners

3. Color the circle red.
Color the square blue.
Color the rectangle green.
Color the triangle yellow.

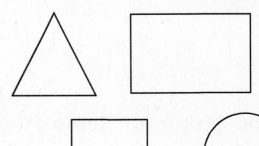

4. Color the cubes blue.
Color the cylinders red.
Color the rectangular prisms yellow.

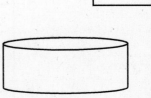

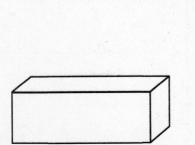 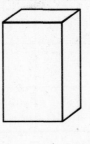 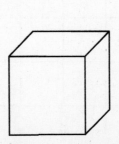 

5. Ring the shape that comes next in the pattern.

6. Ring how the shapes moved.

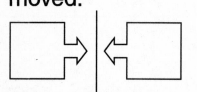

slide

flip

turn

7. Ring how the shapes moved.

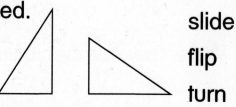

slide

flip

turn

8. Color the middle cylinder.

9. Color the top block.

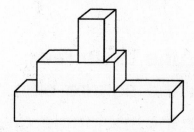

Use the graph for items 10 and 11. Mark these points on the graph.

10. Start at 0. Go → 2.
Go ↑ 2. Make a red dot.

11. Start at 0. Go → 5.
Go ↑ 3. Make a blue dot.

Geometry 1-2, SV 9781419099144

Level Assessment: **Part B, Units 4–5**

Ring the figure that shows a line of symmetry.

12. 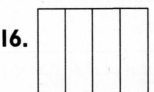   13.

Ring the number of equal parts.

14.
0   4   5

15.
0   2   3

16.
0   3   4

Ring the fraction that tells what part is shaded.

17.
$\frac{1}{3}$ $\frac{1}{4}$ $\frac{1}{5}$

18.
$\frac{1}{2}$ $\frac{2}{3}$ $\frac{2}{4}$

19.
$\frac{1}{4}$ $\frac{2}{4}$ $\frac{3}{4}$

Write each fraction to tell what part of the group is shaded.

20.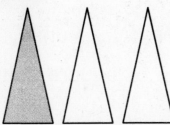

21.

Geometry 1–2, SV 9781419099144

Name _____ Date _____

Level Assessment: **Part B, Units 4–5**

Use an inch ruler to measure each worm.

22. ![worm]

_____ inch

23. ![worm]

_____ inches

Use a centimeter ruler to measure each worm.

24.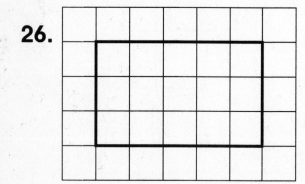

_____ centimeters

25. ![worm]

_____ centimeters

Find the perimeter and area for each rectangle.

26. ![rectangle on grid]

27.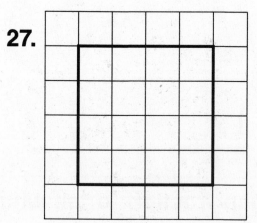

Perimeter = _____ units

Area = _____ square units

Perimeter = _____ units

Area = _____ square units

Level Assessment
Geometry 1–2, SV 9781419099144

LESSON 1   Open and Closed Figures

A gate in a fence can be open.

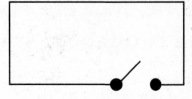

When the gate is closed,
you can not go in or out.

A figure can be **open**.
It does not begin and end at the same point.

A figure can be **closed**.
It begins and ends at the same point.
You can not go in or out of the figure.

 Trace the figure with your finger. If you begin and end
at the same place, the figure is closed.

Open and Closed Figures Practice

Ring the figures that are open in each row.
The first one is done for you.

1.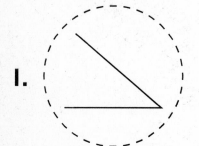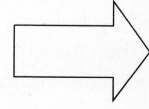

2.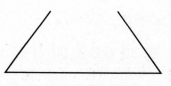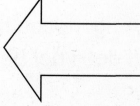

3.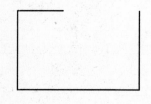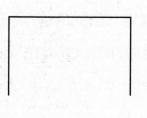

4.

Open and Closed Figures More Practice

Color inside each closed figure.

1.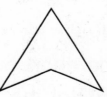

2.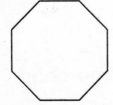

3.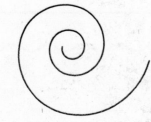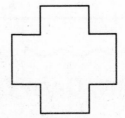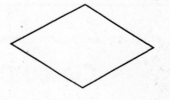

4. Draw a closed figure.   **5.** Draw an open figure.

Closed	Open

Geometry 1–2, SV 9781419099144

Open and Closed Figures Activities

Sorting Letters

Materials: Sorting Chart (page 114), 6 pipe cleaners

Steps to Follow:

1. Look at the chart on page 114.
2. Write **OPEN** at the top of the first column.
3. Write **CLOSED** at the top of the second column.
4. Bend the pipe cleaners to make these letters.

| O | B | C | D | M | L |

5. Sort the letters that you make. Put them in the chart where they belong.
6. Glue the letters onto the chart.

Closed Chains, Open Chains

Materials: 5 thin strips of art paper, glue, 5 pipe cleaners

Steps to Follow:

1. Make a loop with one strip of paper.
2. Glue the ends together.
3. Put another strip of paper through the first loop.
4. Glue the ends of the second loop.
5. Keep making loops until you use all of the paper strips.

Now try to make a chain with pipe cleaners shaped like the letter C. Tell what happens.

LESSON 2   Sides and Corners

A **side** is a straight line of a flat shape.

A **corner** is the place where two lines meet.

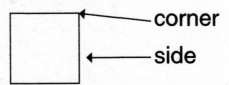

This shape has 4 sides.   It also has 4 corners.

   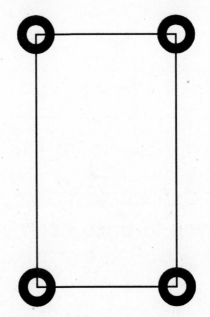

 Hint   A shape with straight sides has the same number of sides and corners.

Unit 1: Plane Figures, Lesson 2
Geometry 1–2, SV 9781419099144

Sides and Corners Practice

1. Draw a ● on each corner.

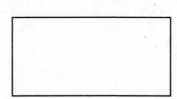
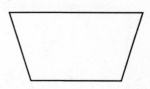

2. Use a red crayon to trace each straight side.

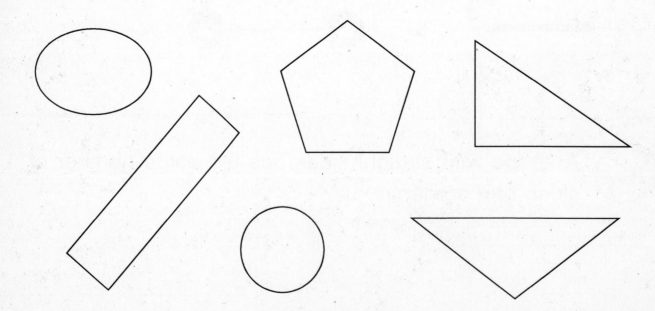

Sides and Corners More Practice

Write how many sides and corners for each shape. The first one is done for you.

Shape	Sides	Corners
1.	3	3
2.		
3.		
4.		
5.		
6.		

15

Sides and Corners Activities

Draw a Shape

Materials: crayons

Steps to Follow:

1. Use the dot grid.
2. Draw a shape that has 4 sides.
3. Make all 4 sides the same length.
4. Write the number of corners.

   _____ corners
5. Color the shape.

Compare Shapes

Steps to Follow:

1. Draw a shape that has sides and corners.
2. Cover the shape.
3. Describe it to a friend.
4. Have your friend draw it.
5. Compare what you drew.

Name _____ Date _____

LESSON 3 Squares and Rectangles

A **square** has 4 corners and 4 sides.

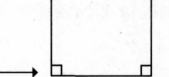

Each corner is a **square corner**. ⟶

Each side is the same length.

A **rectangle** has 4 square corners.

Opposite sides are the same length.

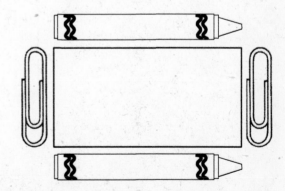

 Hint If you turn a square, it looks like a baseball diamond.

Unit 1: Plane Figures, Lesson 3
Geometry 1–2, SV 9781419099144

Squares and Rectangles Practice

Ring the squares in each row.
The first one is done for you.

1.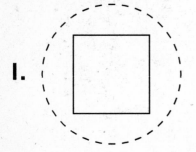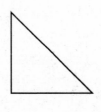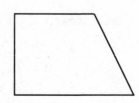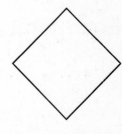

2.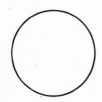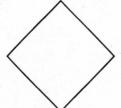

Ring the rectangles in each row.

3.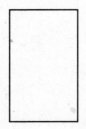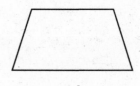

4.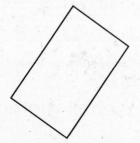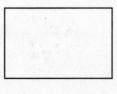

Squares and Rectangles More Practice

Color each square red.
Then color the rectangles blue.

19

Unit 1: Plane Figures, Lesson 3
Geometry 1–2, SV 9781419099144

Squares and Rectangles Activities

Folding Squares and Rectangles

Materials: Flat Shapes (page 115), scissors, envelope

Steps to Follow:

1. Cut out the shapes from page 115.

2. Fold a square so that one pair of opposite corners meets. Show what happens.

3. Try to match opposite corners of a rectangle. What happens now?

4. Explore other ways to fold squares and rectangles.

5. Put all of the shapes in an envelope to use in the next lesson.

Compare Blocks

Materials: 6 to 10 attribute blocks, art paper, pencil

Steps to Follow:

1. Compare blocks by size, color, and shape.

2. Make a group of blocks that have 4 sides and 4 corners.

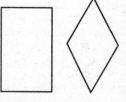

3. Are all of these blocks squares or rectangles? Tell why.

4. Trace one square and one rectangle on art paper.

5. Circle the square corners.

6. Trace one shape that does not have square corners.

LESSON 4   Triangles and Circles

A **triangle** has 3 corners and 3 sides.
There are many kinds of triangles.

 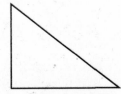 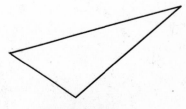

3 sides	3 sides	3 sides
3 corners	3 corners	3 corners

A **circle** has 0 corners.

   It has 0 sides.
   It is round.

0 corners
0 sides

 A circle will almost fill a square.

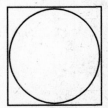

This shape almost fills a rectangle.
It is not a circle.

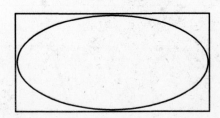

Triangles and Circles Practice

Ring the triangles in each row.
The first one is done for you.

1.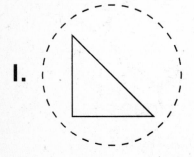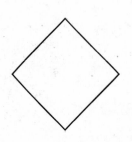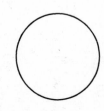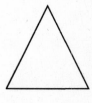

2.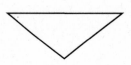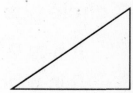

Ring the circles in each row.

3.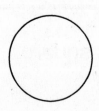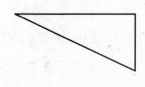

4.

Unit 1: Plane Figures, Lesson 4
Geometry 1–2, SV 9781419099144

Name _____ Date _____

Triangles and Circles More Practice

Color each triangle red.
Color each circle blue.

Unit 1: Plane Figures, Lesson 4
Geometry 1–2, SV 9781419099144

Triangles and Circles Activities

Shape Mask

Materials: paper plates, various colors of art paper, scissors, glue, crayons

Steps to Follow:

1. Cut some triangles and circles from art paper.
2. Make a face with the shapes.
3. Glue the shapes to a paper plate to make a mask.
4. Tell about your mask and the shapes that you used.

Sorting Shapes by Number of Sides

Materials: Sorting Chart (page 114), cut-.out shapes from previous lesson (from page 115), scissors, glue

Steps to Follow:

1. Cut out the shapes on page 115 or use the shapes from the previous lesson.
2. Look at the chart on page 114.
3. Write **3** at the top of the first column.
4. Write **4** at the top of the second column.
5. Sort the shapes by the number of sides.
6. Glue the shapes with 3 sides and with 4 sides on the chart.
7. Tell about the shapes that you have left.

Name _____   Date _____

LESSON 5   Congruent Figures

Congruent figures have the same size and shape.
These figures are congruent.

> They are both rectangles.
> The sides are the same length.
> The corners are the same.

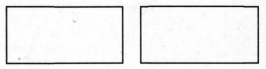

These figures are congruent.

> They are both triangles.
> The sides are the same length.
> The corners are the same.
> They do not have to be turned the same way.

These figures are not congruent.
The corners are not the same.

 Hint Check to see if two figures are congruent. Cut one of the figures out. Place it on top of the other figure. If it is an exact match, the figures are congruent.

Unit 1: Plane Figures, Lesson 5
Geometry 1–2, SV 9781419099144

Congruent Figures Practice

Color the two congruent figures in each row.
The first one is done for you.

1.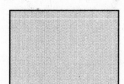

2.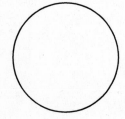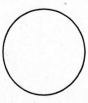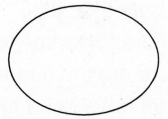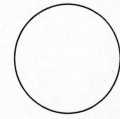

3.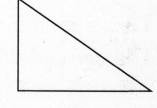

4.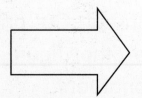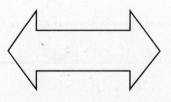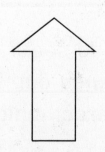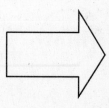

Unit 1: Plane Figures, Lesson 5
Geometry 1–2, SV 9781419099144

Congruent Figures More Practice

Look at the first figure in each row.
Draw a figure that is the same size and shape.
The first one is done for you.

1.

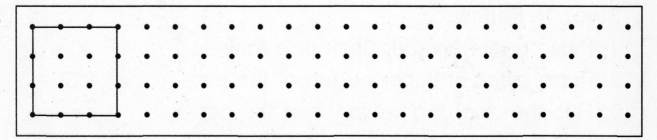

2.

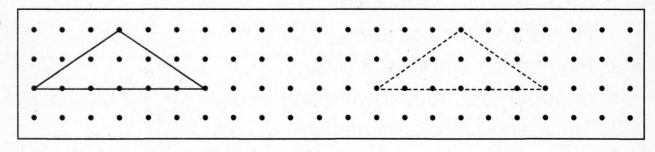

3.

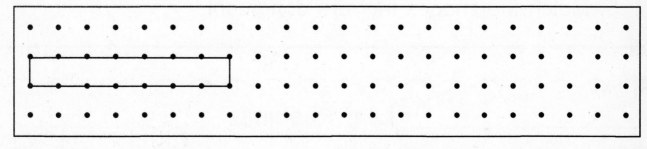

4.

Congruent Figures Activities

Tracing Shapes

Materials: attribute blocks, paper, pencil, scissors

Steps to Follow:

1. Choose 3 blocks that are different shapes or sizes.
2. Place each block on a piece of paper and trace it with your pencil.
3. Trace each block 2 times.
4. Cut out the shapes that you made.
5. Match the shapes that are congruent.

Leaf Rubbings

Materials: leaves, plain paper, crayons, glue

Steps to Follow:

1. Place a leaf on your desk or a table.
2. Put a piece of paper on top of the leaf.
3. Rub the side of a crayon over the paper until the leaf appears.
4. Use a different leaf to make one more leaf rubbing on the paper.
5. Now glue each leaf next to the print that it made.
6. Draw a line between the congruent leaves.

Assessment: Plane Figures

1. Ring the figures that are open.

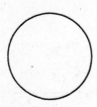  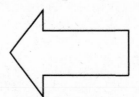 

2. Write the number of sides and corners.

  _____ sides

_____ corners

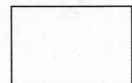 _____ sides

_____ corners

3. Color the circles red.
Color the square blue.
Color the rectangles green.
Color the triangles yellow.

4. Draw a figure that is the same size and shape.

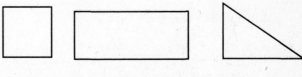

Name _____ Date _____

LESSON 6   Footprints

When you walk in sand, you make **footprints**.

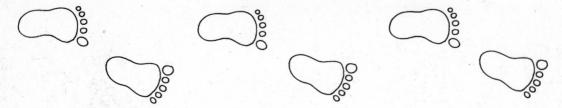

Some solid figures have footprints.

If you press a block into sand, it will make a footprint.

A footprint is the shape of the flat side.

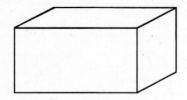

This footprint is a rectangle.

You can make a footprint with any flat side.

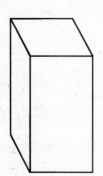

This footprint is a square.

 Hint A basketball does not have a flat side.
It does not have a footprint.

Name _____ Date _____

Footprints Practice

Ring the footprint of each shape.
The first one is done for you.

1.	
2.	
3.	
4.	
5.	

Unit 2: Solid Figures, Lesson 6
Geometry 1–2, SV 9781419099144

Name _____ Date _____

Footprints More Practice

Draw lines to match footprints and solid shapes.

1.

a.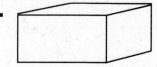

2.

b.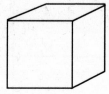

3.

c.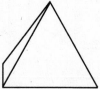

4.

d.

How many ◯ are on each shape? Write the number.

5. 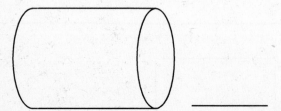 _____

6. 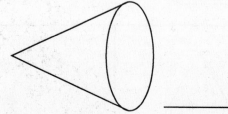 _____

Footprints Activities

Footprints in Clay

Materials: clay, blocks

Steps to Follow:

1. Roll out and press clay to make a flat space to work.
2. Choose 3 or 4 blocks that have a flat side.
3. Press the blocks into the clay to make footprints.
4. Show the footprints to a friend.
5. Match the blocks and the footprints.

Tracing Footprints

Materials: blocks, paper, pencil

Steps to Follow:

1. Choose 2 blocks.
2. Put the blocks on your paper.
3. Trace each footprint with a pencil.
4. Show the footprints to a friend.
5. Match the blocks and the footprints.

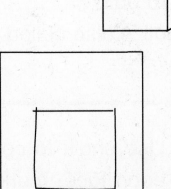

Name _____ Date _____

LESSON 7   Boxes and Balls

Boxes are **rectangular prisms**.
Each flat part is called a **face**.
The footprint of each face is a
rectangle or a square.

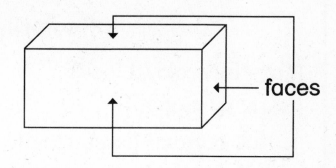

faces

Some boxes are **cubes**.
Every face is a square.
The straight lines that make
each face are called **edges**.

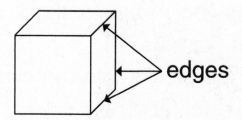

edges

Rectangular prisms and cubes have 6 faces.
Rectangular prisms and cubes have 12 edges.

There is a solid shape that has 0 faces.

It has 0 edges.
It is a ball.
A ball is also called a **sphere**.

Hint Use chalk to count the faces on a box. As you count
each face, mark it with chalk. That way, you will not
count the same face twice. Do the same thing to
count edges.

Boxes and Balls Practice

1. Color the cubes green.

2. Color the rectangular prisms purple.

3. Color the spheres yellow.

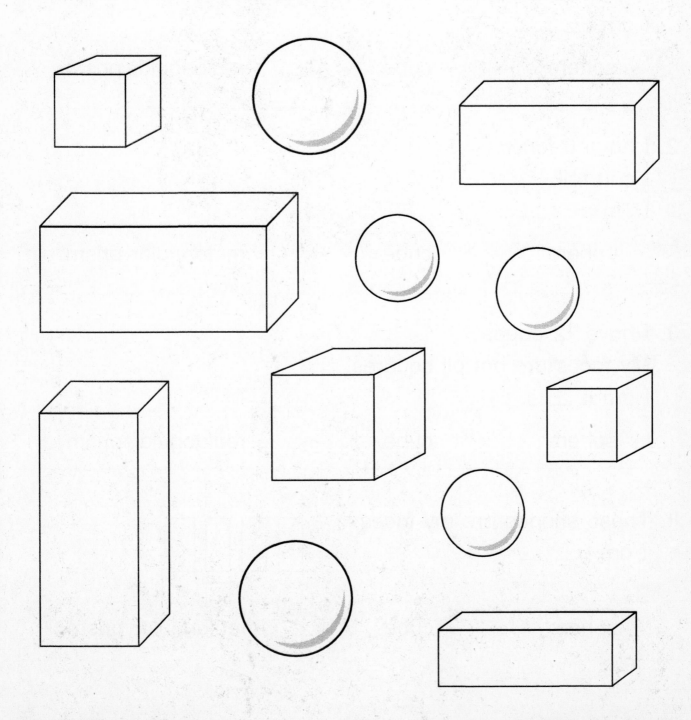

Unit 2: Solid Figures, Lesson 7
Geometry 1–2, SV 9781419099144

Boxes and Balls More Practice

Ring the answer to each riddle.

1. I have 6 faces.
My faces are all squares.
I am a _____.

    sphere   cube   rectangular prism

2. I have 0 faces.
I can roll.
I am a _____.

    sphere   cube   rectangular prism

3. I have 12 edges.
My faces are not all squares.
I am a _____.

    sphere   cube   rectangular prism

4. These shapes are my faces.
I am a _____.

    sphere   cube   rectangular prism

Boxes and Balls Activities

Make a Cube

Materials: Cube Net (page 116), scissors, clear tape

Steps to Follow:

1. Cut out the shape that is on page 116.
2. Cut only the dashed lines.
3. Fold along each solid line.
4. Fold the shape into a cube.
5. Tape the cube together.

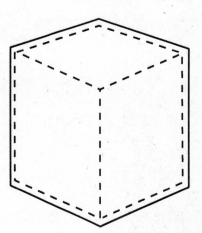

Treasure Hunt

Materials: Sorting Chart (page 114), pencil

Steps to Follow:

1. Look at the chart on page 114.
2. Write **BOXES** at the top of the first column.
3. Write **BALLS** at the top of the second column.
4. Look around the room.
5. When you see a box, write an **X** under **BOXES**.
6. When you see a ball, write an **X** under **BALLS**.
7. Did you see more boxes or more balls?

37

Name _____ Date _____

LESSON 8   Cans and Cones

Cans are **cylinders**.
Each flat part is a face.
The footprint of each face is a circle.
Cylinders have 2 faces.

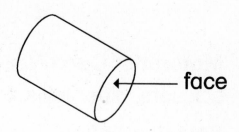 face

There is a solid shape that has only 1 face.
The other end is a point.
It is a **cone**.

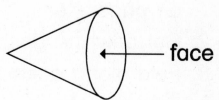 face

How many edges are on a cylinder?

    Edges are straight lines.
    A cylinder has 0 edges.

 point

How many edges are on a cone?

    A cone has 0 edges.

How many points are on a cylinder? 0

How many points are on a cone? 1

 Hint A cylinder, a cone, and a sphere will roll. The parts that roll are not called faces. Faces are flat.

Unit 2: Solid Figures, Lesson 8
Geometry 1–2, SV 9781419099144

Cans and Cones Practice

1. Color the cylinders blue.

2. Color the cones orange.

3. Draw an **X** on the shapes that are not cylinders or cones.

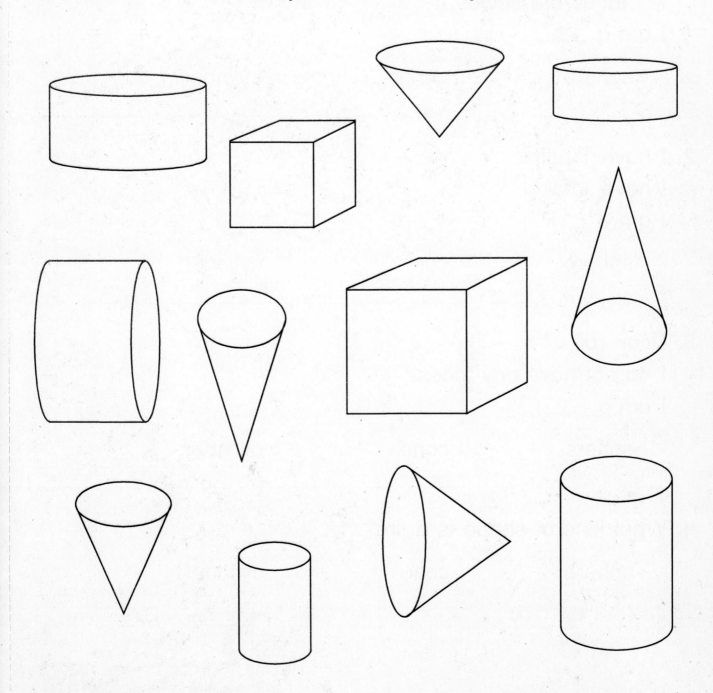

39

Unit 2: Solid Figures, Lesson 8
Geometry 1–2, SV 9781419099144

Cans and Cones More Practice

Ring the answer to each riddle.

1. I have 2 faces.
My faces are circles.
I am a ____.

　　sphere　　　　　cone　　　　　cylinder

2. I have 1 point.
I have 1 face.
I am a ____.

　　sphere　　　　　cone　　　　　cylinder

3. I can roll.
I do not have any faces.
I am a ____.

　　sphere　　　　　cone　　　　　cylinder

4. What kind of shape is a tire?

　　sphere　　　　　cone　　　　　cylinder

Unit 2: Solid Figures, Lesson 8
Geometry 1–2, SV 9781419099144

Cans and Cones Activities

Make a Can

Materials: empty paper roll, art paper, pencil, scissors, clear tape

Steps to Follow:

1. Stand an empty paper roll on your art paper.
2. Trace around the bottom to draw 2 circles.
3. Cut out the circles.
4. Tape a circle on each end of the empty paper roll.
5. Compare the can that you made to other cylinders that you find.

How Does It Roll?

Materials: sphere, can, and cone blocks; paper bag

Steps to Follow:

1. Put a sphere, a can, and a cone into a large paper bag.
2. Reach inside the bag and feel one block. Do not look.
3. Tell someone about the block that you feel.
4. Tell if the block rolls every way or just one way.
5. Have someone guess the block.
6. Take the block out of the bag to see if the guess was right.
7. Take turns to play again and again.

Name _____ Date _____

LESSON 9   Identifying Solids

You can identify solid figures by their faces and edges.
You can also count the **corners**.
A corner is the point where edges meet.

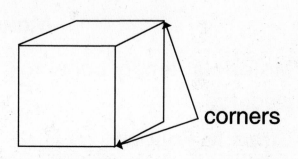
corners

Shape	Faces	Edges	Corners
	6	12	8
	6	12	8
	0	0	0
	2	0	0
	1	0	0

 Hint A cone has a point, but it does not have a corner.
A corner is at the end of a straight edge.

Unit 2: Solid Figures, Lesson 9
Geometry 1–2, SV 9781419099144

Name _____ Date _____

Identifying Solids Practice

1. Color the shapes that have 8 corners.

2. Ring the shapes that have faces that are circles.

3. Draw an **X** on the shapes that have 0 faces.

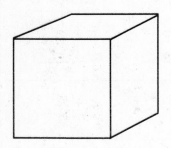  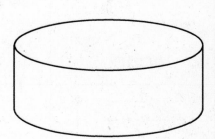

 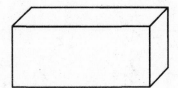

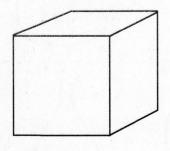 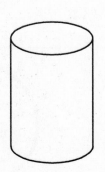 

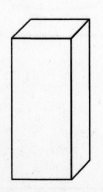 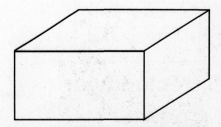

Unit 2: Solid Figures, Lesson 9
Geometry 1–2, SV 9781419099144

Identifying Solids More Practice

Ring the matching shape in each row.

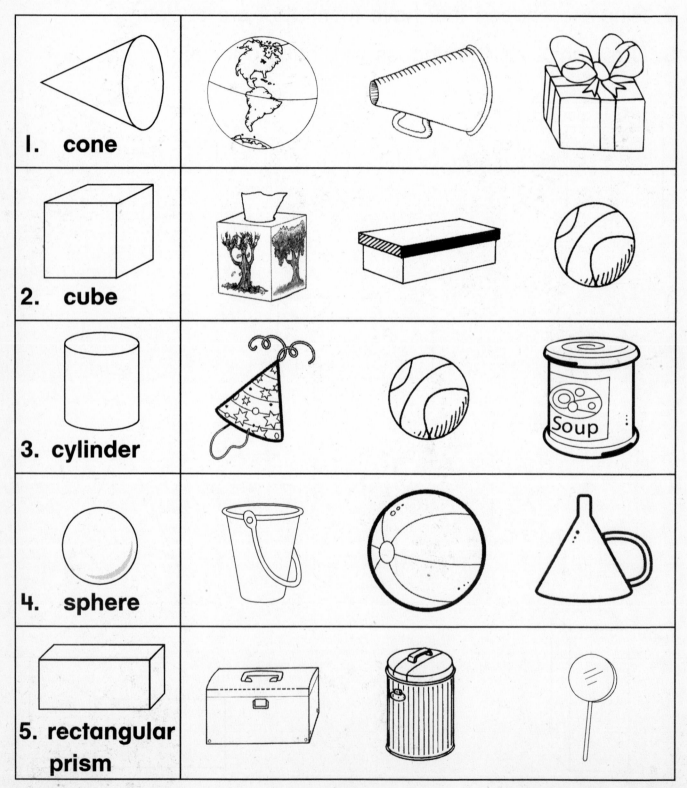

1. cone

2. cube

3. cylinder

4. sphere

5. rectangular prism

Unit 2: Solid Figures, Lesson 9
Geometry 1–2, SV 9781419099144

Identifying Solids Activities

Build and Copy Shapes

Materials: building blocks, Solid Shapes (page 117), scissors, glue, art paper

Steps to Follow:

1. Use at least 6 blocks to make a building.
2. Cut out the pictures of blocks from page 117.
3. Use the pictures of blocks to copy your building.
4. Glue the pictures of blocks to art paper.
5. Compare your building and your art paper.
6. They should look alike.

Shapes in a Bag

Materials: blocks, paper bag

Steps to Follow:

1. Put 4 or 5 building blocks into a large paper bag.
2. Reach inside the bag and feel one block. Do not look.
3. Tell someone about the block that you feel.
4. Tell about faces, edges, and corners.
5. Have someone guess the block.
6. Take the block out of the bag to see if the guess was right.
7. Take turns to play again and again.

Name _____ Date _____

LESSON 10   Patterns

A **pattern** repeats so that you can tell what comes next.
You can use shapes to make a pattern.

What part of the pattern repeats? CIRCLE, RECTANGLE

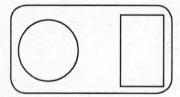 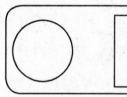 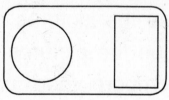

If the pattern keeps going, the next shape will be a circle.

You can use blocks to make a pattern.

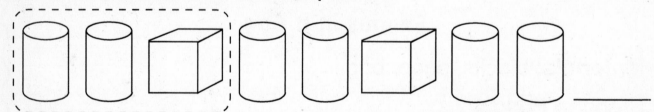

What part of the pattern repeats? CAN, CAN, CUBE

If the pattern keeps going, the next block will be a cube.

 In each pattern, ring the part that repeats.
Then you will know what comes next.

Unit 2: Solid Figures, Lesson 10
Geometry 1–2, SV 9781419099144

Patterns Practice

Ring the shape that shows what comes next.
The first one is done for you.

1.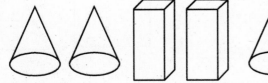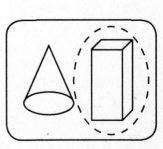

2.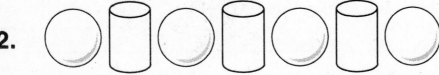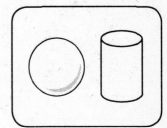

3.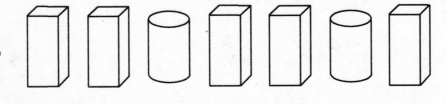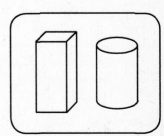

4.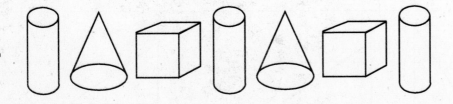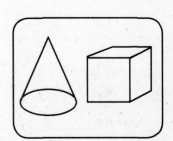

Unit 2: Solid Figures, Lesson 10
Geometry 1–2, SV 9781419099144

Patterns More Practice

Draw the shape that is missing in each pattern.
The first one is done for you.

1.

2.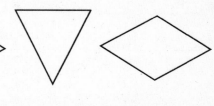

3.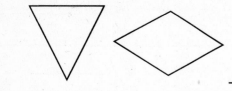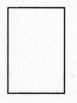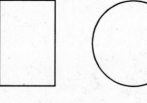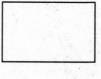

4.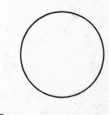

5.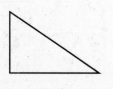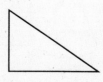

Unit 2: Solid Figures, Lesson 10
Geometry 1–2, SV 9781419099144

Patterns Activities

Pipe Cleaner Patterns

Materials: pipe cleaners, art paper, glue

Steps to Follow:

1. Bend pipe cleaners to make circles and triangles.
2. Make a pattern with the circles and triangles.
3. Glue your pattern onto art paper.
4. Ask a friend to tell what comes next.
5. Add to your pattern or make a new one.

Game: What's Missing?

Materials: building blocks

Steps to Follow:

1. Choose two kinds of blocks.
2. Make a pattern with 6 to 10 blocks.
3. Then take one of the blocks away.
4. Ask a friend to tell what is missing.
5. Then put the block back into the pattern.
6. Take turns hiding a block and guessing what is missing.

49

Name _____   Date _____

Assessment: Solid Figures

1. Ring the shape that is on the bottom of the cone.

cone

2. Color the cubes blue.
   Draw an **X** on the cylinders.

          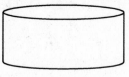   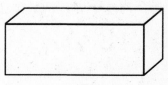

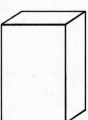   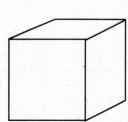   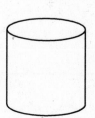

3. Ring the shape that comes next in the pattern.

  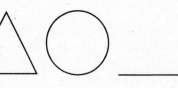 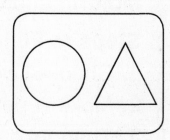

4. Draw the shape that is missing in the pattern.

          _____

Geometry 1–2, SV 9781419099144

LESSON 11   Slides, Flips, and Turns

When you sit at the top of a slide and push off,
you are still sitting when you get to the bottom.

A shape can move the same way.
In a **slide**, the shape moves along a line.
It does not change in any other way.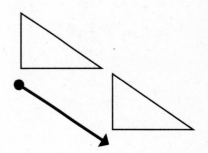

A shape can be flipped.
A **flip** moves a figure over a line.
It looks like a mirror picture of the shape.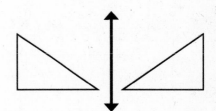

A shape can also be turned.
A **turn** moves a figure around a point.
It does not change size or shape.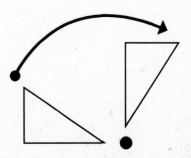

 Hint Show how a book can move across your desk.
If it does not turn a different direction or flip over,
it moves in a slide.

Slides, Flips, and Turns Practice

Ring the word that shows how the shapes moved.
The first one is done for you.

1.    slide

    flip

    (turn)

2. 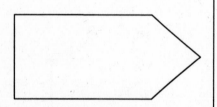   slide

    flip

    turn

3. 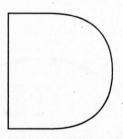   slide

    flip

    turn

4.    slide

    flip

    turn

52

Slides, Flips, and Turns More Practice

1. Draw a slide of the shape.

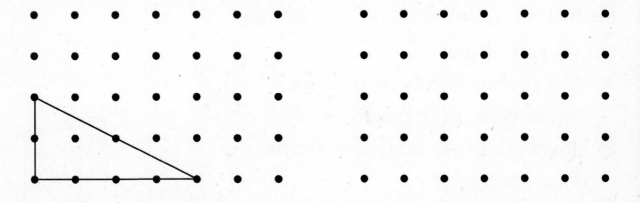

2. Draw a flip of the shape.

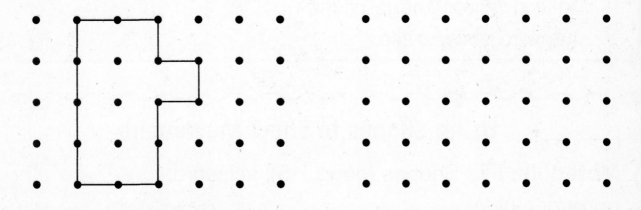

3. Draw a turn of the shape.

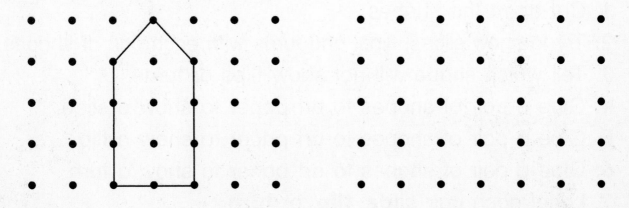

Unit 3: Movement and Location, Lesson 11
Geometry 1–2, SV 9781419099144

Slides, Flips, and Turns Activities

Geoboard Shapes

Materials: geoboards, rubber bands

Steps to Follow:

1. Use rubber bands to make a shape on a geoboard.
2. Have a partner copy the shape on a geoboard.
3. Use the geoboards to show a slide or a turn.
4. Make a mirror image of the shape to show a flip.

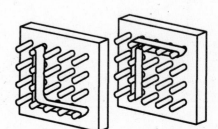

Using Shapes to Show Movement

Materials: Flat Shapes (page 115), scissors, art paper, glue

Steps to Follow:

1. Cut apart the shapes.
2. Try to show slides, flips, and turns with each pair of shapes.
3. Tell which shape will not show flips or turns.
4. Glue a pair of shapes to art paper to show a slide.
5. Glue a pair of shapes to art paper to show a flip.
6. Glue a pair of shapes to art paper to show a turn.
7. Label each pair **slide**, **flip**, or **turn**.

LESSON 12   Cutting and Combining Shapes

What shapes can you make by cutting a rectangle?
You might make two smaller rectangles.

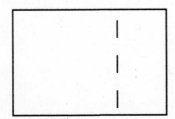

You might make two triangles.

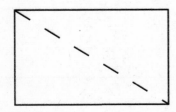

How can you put shapes together in new ways?
Trace the two triangles in the rectangle above.
Turn them to make a larger triangle.

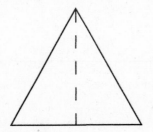

 To make the big triangle above, you have to flip one of the small triangles over.

Cutting and Combining Shapes Practice

Look at the first figure in each row.
If you cut it along the dashed line, what will it make?
Ring the new figure.

1.

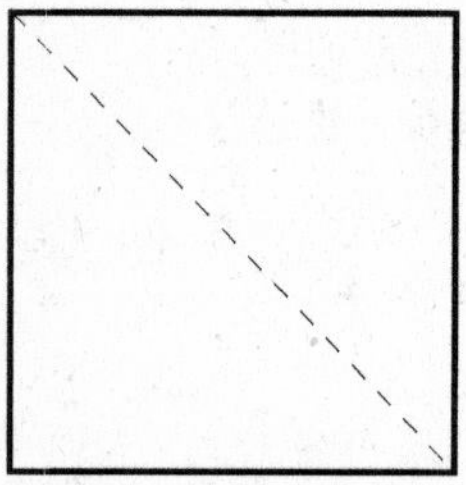

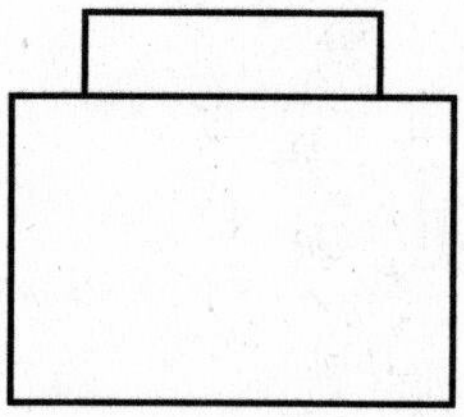

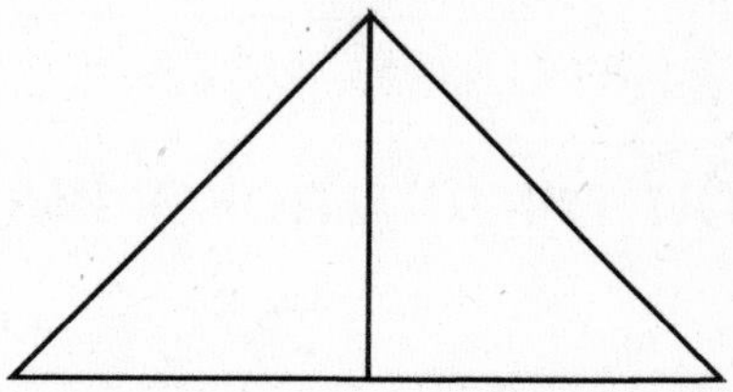

2.

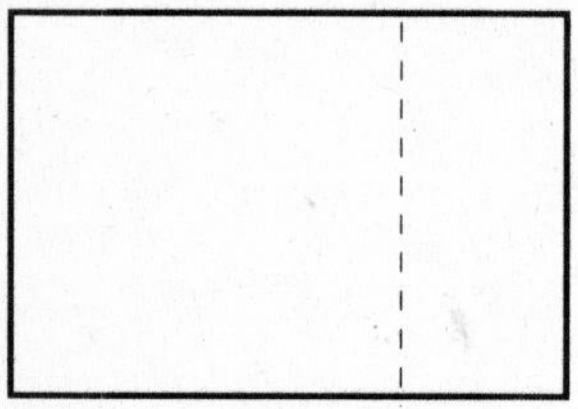

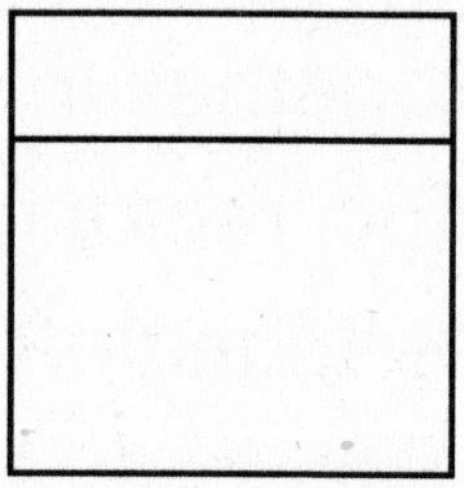

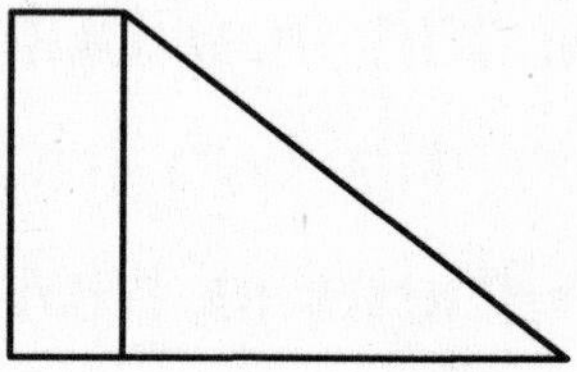

3.

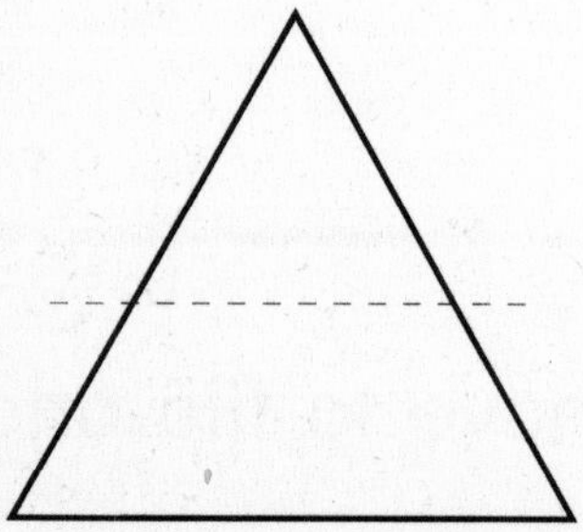

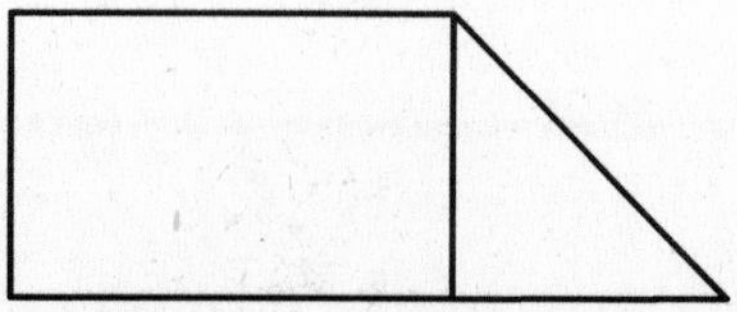

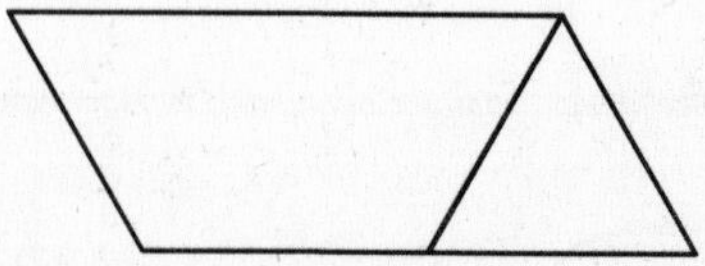

56

Cutting and Combining Shapes More Practice

Put two shapes together in each row.
Turn or flip the shapes if you wish.
Draw your new shape.

I.

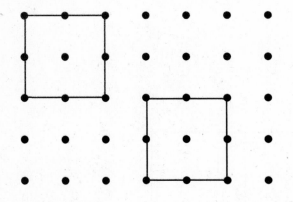

2.

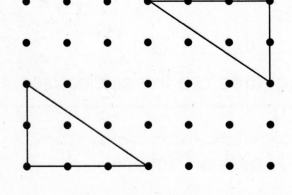

3.

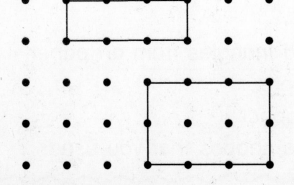

Cutting and Combining Shapes Activities

Finding Shapes

Materials: crayons

Steps to Follow:

1. Look at the picture below.
2. Can you find 8 squares?
3. Can you find 12 triangles?
4. Trace or color the shapes.

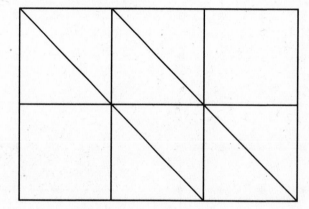

Hint: Not all of the triangles or squares are the same size.

Cutting Shapes to Make a Picture

Materials: color sheets of art paper, scissors, glue, plain paper

Steps to Follow:

1. Cut squares, rectangles, and triangles from art paper.
2. Make a design with the shapes.
3. Glue your design to plain paper.
4. Ask a friend to find all of the shapes that you used.

Name _____ Date _____

LESSON **13** **Relative Position**

Where does everything go?

Use position words to tell where to place something.

Look at the blocks.

The cone is on the **top** of the blocks.
It is **above** the can.

The cube is on the **bottom** of the blocks.
It is **below** the can.

The can is in the **middle** of the blocks.

Look at the blocks now.

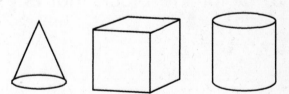

The cone is **beside** the cube.

The can is **beside** the cube.

The cube is in the **middle**.

 Hint There might be many ways to tell where
to set something.

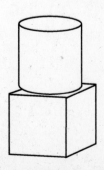

The can in this picture is on top of the cube.

It is above the cube.

It is also over the cube.

Geometry 1–2, SV 9781419099144

Relative Position Practice

1. Color the block that is on the bottom.

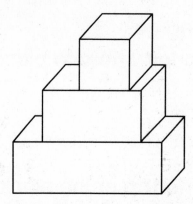

2. Color the block that is in the middle.

3. Color the block that is in the middle.

4. Color the block that is on the top.

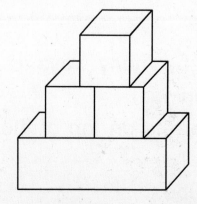

Relative Position More Practice

1. Draw a circle in the box above the R.

2. Draw a square in the box below the T.

R	**S**	**T**

3. Draw a triangle in the box below the A.

4. Draw a circle in the box next to the triangle.

A	**B**	**C**

5. Write **X** in the box above the circle.

6. Write **Z** in the middle box in the bottom row.

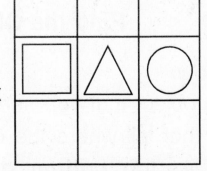

7. Write **S** in the box beside the circle.

8. Write **W** in the box next to the square.

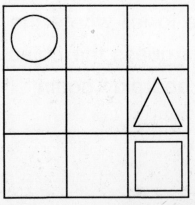

Relative Position Activities

Placing Objects

Materials: A Place for Everything (page 118), scissors, glue

Steps to Follow:

1. Look at the bookshelf that is on page 118.
2. Cut out the pictures that are below the bookshelf.
3. Place the pictures on the shelves and cover your work.
4. Tell a friend where to place his or her pictures to match.
5. Check. Are your pictures in the same places?
6. Try again. Take turns.
7. Glue the pictures on the shelves when you are done.

Find the Object

Steps to Follow:

1. Choose an object that you see in the room.
2. Give clues that tell where the object is sitting.
3. Use words like **top**, **bottom**, **above**, **below**, **beside**, and **middle** to tell where the object is.
4. Have others guess the object.
5. Take turns and play again.

LESSON 14   Points on a Line

A **line** is straight.
It has arrows to show that it never ends.

A **line segment** is straight.
It has **points** to show where it ends.

A line segment can be a part of a line.
It is the part between two points.

You can use points on a line to name a place.
On a **number line**, each place has its own number.

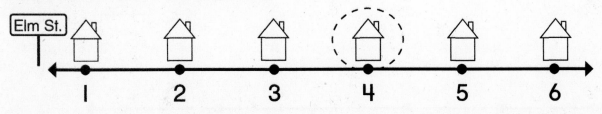

1   2   3   4   5   6

A map uses lines to name places.
Chad's house is at 4 Elm Street.
Point to where Chad lives.

1   2   3   4   5   6

Hint Use words like **beside, next to, between, left,** and **right** to tell how to find Chad's house. His house is next to 5 Elm Street. It is between houses 3 and 5.

Points on a Line Practice

1. Draw a ring around the line.

2. Draw a ring around the line segment.

Complete each number line.

3.

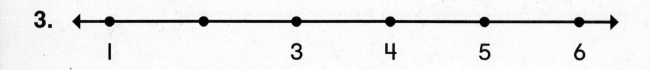

4.

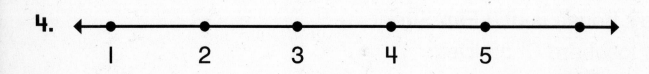

5.

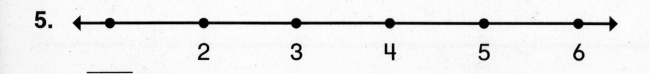

Points on a Line More Practice

Color to show each house that is named.

1. Amy's house is between house 3 and house 5.
Which one is Amy's house?

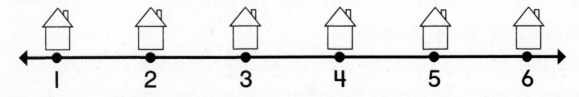

2. Evan's house is beside house 6.
Which one is Evan's house?

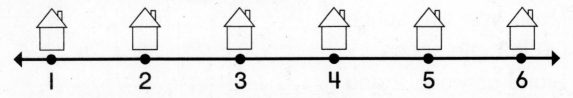

3. Jason's house is next to house 2.
It is not house 1.
Which one is Jason's house?

4. Kami's house is house 2.
Raul's house is four houses away.
Which one is Raul's house?

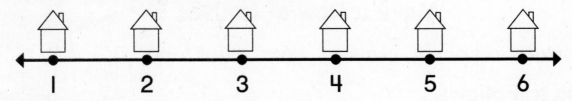

65

Name _____ Date _____

Points on a Line Activities

Giving Directions on a Number Line

Materials: plain paper, marker

Steps to Follow:

1. Write a number on five pieces of paper.
   Write **1**, **2**, **3**, **4**, and **5**.
2. Put the papers on the floor to show a paper number line.
3. Have a partner stand by one of the numbers.
4. Give directions to tell your partner where to move.
   Here are some ideas.
   - Move over two spaces.
   - Go left one space.
   - Stand between 2 and 4.

1	2	3	4	5

5. Take turns giving directions.

Make a Row of Houses

Materials: art paper, crayons, yarn, clear tape

Steps to Follow:

1. Hang a long piece of yarn or string across a wall.
2. Draw and color a house on art paper.
3. Tape your picture onto the yarn.
4. Ask others to tape their pictures onto the yarn.
5. Give directions to go from one house to another.
6. Tell how to find your picture.

LESSON 15 Points on a Graph

You have named points on a line.
Now you will name points on a map.

A **graph** is a map that
shows spaces that are
the same size.
To find a point on a
graph, start at 0.

Go right. →

Then go up. ↑

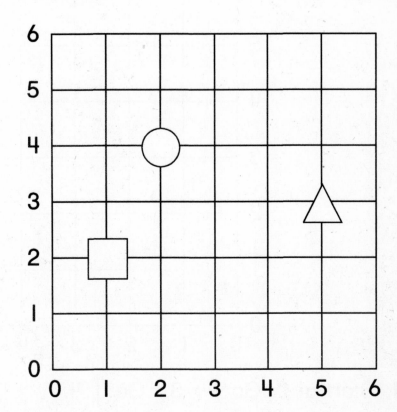

Find ☐. Go → 1. Go ↑ 2.

Find ◯. Go → 2. Go ↑ 4.

Find △. Go → 5. Go ↑ 3.

 Hint Always start at 0 to find a place on a graph.

67

Points on a Graph Practice

Draw a dot for each point.

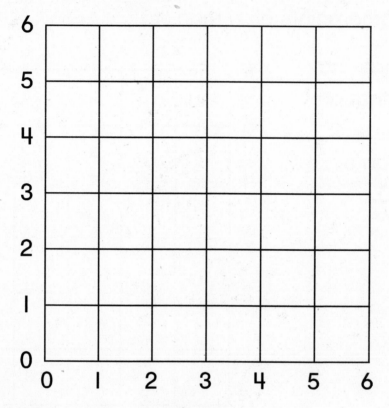

1. Start at 0. Go → 3. Go ↑ 4.
Draw a blue dot to mark the point.

2. Start at 0. Go → 1. Go ↑ 6.
Draw a red dot to mark the point.

3. Start at 0. Go → 6. Go ↑ 1.
Draw a black dot to mark the point.

4. Start at 0. Go → 4. Go ↑ 3.
Draw a yellow dot to mark the point.

5. Start at 0. Go → 5. Go ↑ 2.
Draw a green dot to mark the point.

6. Start at 0. Go → 2. Go ↑ 5.
Draw a brown dot to mark the point.

Points on a Graph More Practice

Ring the correct answer.

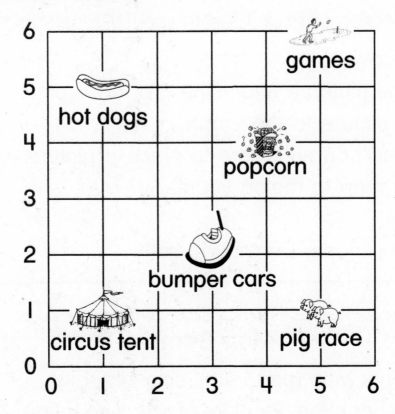

1. Start at 0. Go → 5. Go ↑ 1.　Where are you?

pig race　　hot dogs

2. Start at 0. Go → 4. Go ↑ 4.　Where are you?

bumper cars　　popcorn

3. Start at 0. Go → 5. Go ↑ 6.　Where are you?

games　　pig race

4. Start at 0. Go → 1. Go ↑ 1.　Where are you?

hot dogs　　circus tent

Points on a Graph Activities

Matching Maps

Materials: copies of Park Map (page 119), scissors, glue

Steps to Follow:

1. Cut out the pictures under the graph on page 119.
2. Glue one picture to the graph.
3. Tell a game partner where to place a picture on his or her map to match yours.
4. Take turns.
5. Check your maps. Do they match?

Map Game

Materials: Park Map (page 119), scissors, glue, crayons, number cube, 2 colors of small counting cubes, game playing pieces

Steps to Follow:

1. Use page 119 to make a map for a game.
2. Choose a color of cubes to use.
3. Start at 0. Toss a number cube.
4. Move across, up, or down to match the number on the cube.
5. When you land on a place in the park, put a small cube there.
6. The winner is the one who visits all places in the park first.

Name _____ Date _____

Assessment: Movement and Location

1. Ring how the shapes moved.

slide
flip
turn

2. Ring how the shapes moved.

slide
flip
turn

---

3. Ring the shape that can be made from the first two shapes.

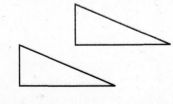 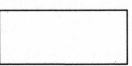 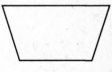

---

4. Color the middle block.

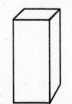

5. Color the top block.

Mark these points on the graph.

6. Start at 0. Go → 3.
Go ↑ 2. Make a red dot.

7. Start at 0. Go → 6.
Go ↑ 4. Make a blue dot.

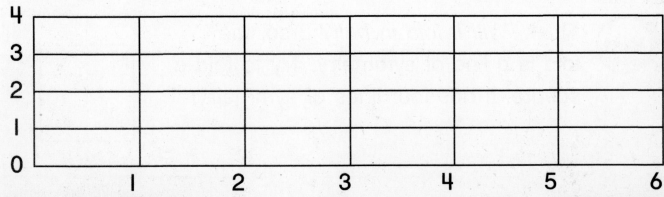

Geometry 1–2, SV 9781419099144

LESSON 16   Lines of Symmetry

A **line of symmetry** divides a figure in half.
Each half looks like a mirror image of the other half.

Look at the lines in these figures.
Each half is the same.
They show lines of symmetry.

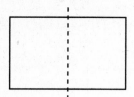   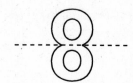

lines of symmetry

Look at the lines in these figures.
Each half is not the same.
They do NOT show lines of symmetry.

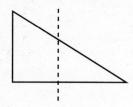   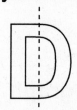   

NOT lines of symmetry

 Think, *Will it fold in half?* If so, the fold is a line of symmetry. Try to fold a square. It has four lines of symmetry!

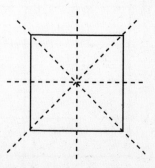

Lines of Symmetry Practice

**Ring the figure that shows a line of symmetry.
The first one has been done for you.**

1.

2.

3.

4.

5.

6.

7.

8.

Geometry 1–2, SV 9781419099144

Lines of Symmetry More Practice

**Draw a line of symmetry for each shape.
The first one has been done for you.**

1. C	2. W	3. Y

4.	5.	6.
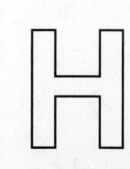		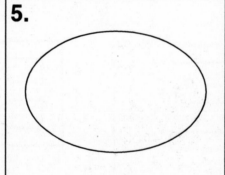

7.	8.	9.
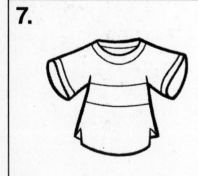	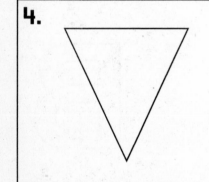	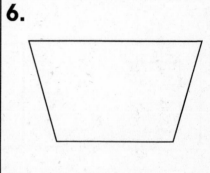

10.	11. H	12.
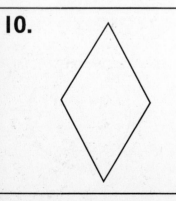		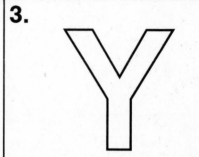

Unit 4: Equal Parts, Lesson 16
Geometry 1–2, SV 9781419099144

Lines of Symmetry Activities

Fold and Cut Shapes

Materials: art paper, scissors, crayons

Steps to Follow:
1. Fold art paper in half.
2. Draw half of a shape from the fold.
3. Cut along your drawing.
4. Unfold the art paper. The fold is a line of symmetry.
5. Color the shape to keep it the same on both sides of the fold.

Mirror Names

Materials: art paper, crayons

Steps to Follow:
1. Fold art paper in half.
2. Write your name along the fold.
3. Use dark crayon markings to trace your name.
4. Unfold the paper. Fold it again with your name inside.
5. Rub hard on the outside of the paper.
6. Unfold the paper. You will see a mirror of your name.

LESSON 17   One Half and One Third

Some figures can be cut into equal parts.

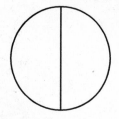   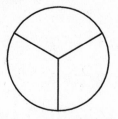

2 equal parts   3 equal parts

When there are 2 equal parts, the parts are called **halves**.
Each part is called **one half**.
Each of these figures shows one half shaded.

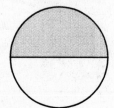   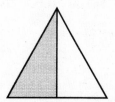

When there are 3 equal parts, the parts are called **thirds**.
Each part is called **one third**.
Each of these figures shows one third shaded.

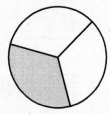      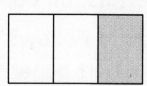

 These figures show 0 equal
parts. They are not halves.
They are not thirds.

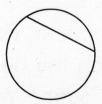   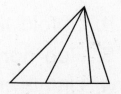

Unit 4: Equal Parts, Lesson 17
Geometry 1–2, SV 9781419099144

One Half and One Third Practice

Ring the number of equal parts.
The first one has been done for you.

1. 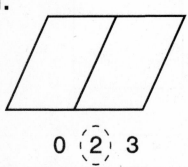 0 (2) 3	2. 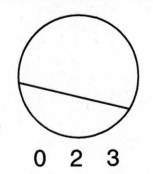 0 2 3	3. 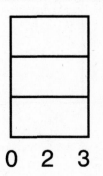 0 2 3
4. 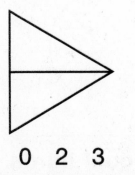 0 2 3	5. 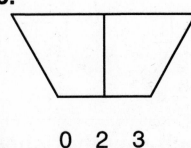 0 2 3	6.  0 2 3
7. 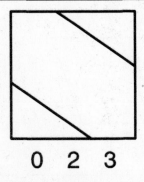 0 2 3	8.  0 2 3	9. 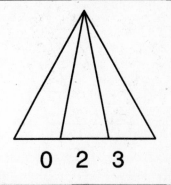 0 2 3
10. 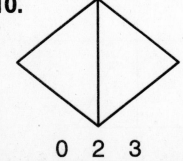 0 2 3	11. 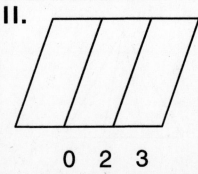 0 2 3	12. 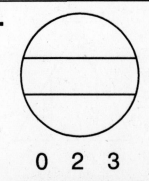 0 2 3

Unit 4: Equal Parts, Lesson 17
Geometry 1–2, SV 9781419099144

One Half and One Third More Practice

Color the shape in each row that shows equal halves.

I.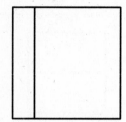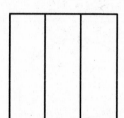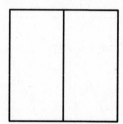

2.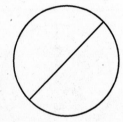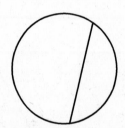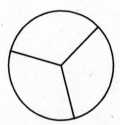

Color the shape in each row that shows equal thirds.

3.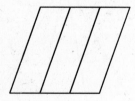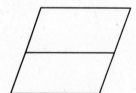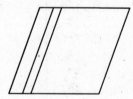

4.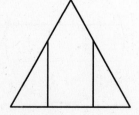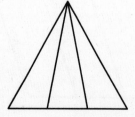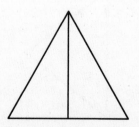

One Half and One Third Activities

Folding and Drawing Halves

Materials: art paper, scissors, pencil, ruler

Steps to Follow:

1. Cut 3 squares out of art paper.

2. Fold each square a different way to show equal halves.

3. Draw lines in the squares below to show how you made halves.

4. Use a ruler to help you draw straight lines.

Folding and Drawing Thirds

Materials: art paper, scissors, pencil, ruler

Steps to Follow:

1. Cut 2 squares out of art paper.

2. Fold each square a different way to show equal thirds.

3. Draw lines in the squares at right to show how you made thirds.

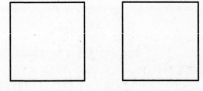

4. Use a ruler to help you draw straight lines.

Unit 4: Equal Parts, Lesson 17
Geometry 1–2, SV 9781419099144

LESSON 18   One Fourth and One Fifth

Some figures can be cut into 4 or 5 equal parts.

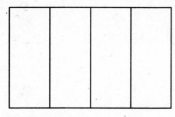

4 equal parts

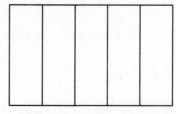

5 equal parts

When there are 4 equal parts, the parts are called **fourths**.
Each part is called **one fourth**.
Each of these figures shows one fourth shaded.

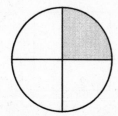

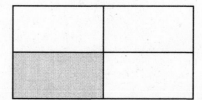

When there are 5 equal parts, the parts are called **fifths**.
Each part is called **one fifth**.
Each of these figures shows one fifth shaded.

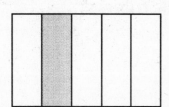

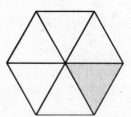

 Hint   These figures show 0 equal parts. They are not fourths. They are not fifths.

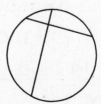

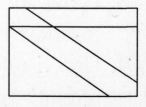

One Fourth and One Fifth Practice

Ring the number of equal parts.
The first one has been done for you.

I.  0 4 ⑤	**2.** 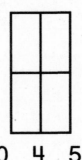 0 4 5	**3.** 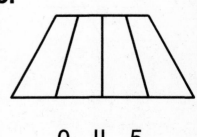 0 4 5
4. 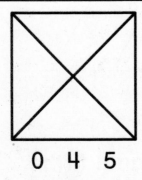 0 4 5	**5.** 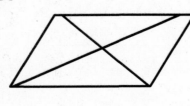 0 4 5	**6.** 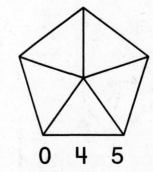 0 4 5
7.  0 4 5	**8.** 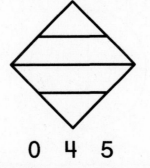 0 4 5	**9.** 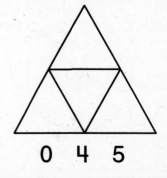 0 4 5
10. 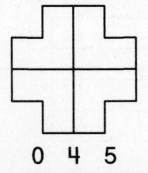 0 4 5	**II.** 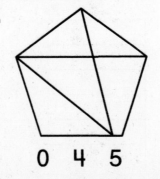 0 4 5	**12.** 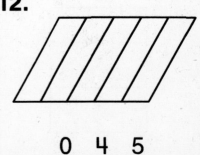 0 4 5

Unit 4: Equal Parts, Lesson 18
Geometry 1–2, SV 9781419099144

One Fourth and One Fifth More Practice

Color the shape in each row that shows equal fourths.

1.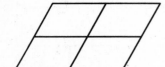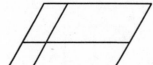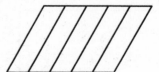

2.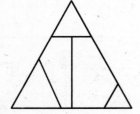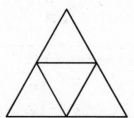

Color the shape in each row that shows equal fifths.

3.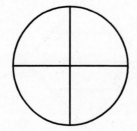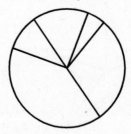

4.

One Fourth and One Fifth Activities

Picture Frame Fourths

Materials: plain paper, crayons

Steps to Follow:

1. Fold a piece of plain paper in half.
2. Then fold it in half again.
3. Unfold the paper to show four equal fourths.
4. Glue or draw a picture in each fourth of the page.
5. Draw and color a picture frame around each picture.

Five Fifths

Materials: 2 number cubes, 5 beans or counters for each player

Steps to Follow:

1. Toss 2 number cubes and add the numbers.
2. If you get the right answer, place a bean on one fifth of the rectangle below.
3. Take turns.
4. The winner is the one who is first to place a bean on all five fifths.
5. Play again. Take turns being the first player.

Name _____ Date _____

LESSON 19   Reading Fractions

A **fraction** names equal parts.
One half and one fourth are fractions.

Count how many parts are shaded.
Count how many equal parts in all.

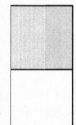

$\dfrac{\text{1 part is shaded.}}{\text{2 equal parts in all.}}$

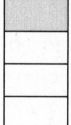

$\dfrac{\text{1 part is shaded.}}{\text{4 equal parts in all.}}$

Write this fraction $\frac{1}{2}$.

Write this fraction $\frac{1}{4}$.

Sometimes more than one part is shaded.
Look below at two thirds and three fifths.

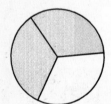

$\dfrac{\text{2 parts are shaded.}}{\text{3 equal parts in all.}}$

$\dfrac{\text{3 parts are shaded.}}{\text{5 equal parts in all.}}$

Write this fraction $\frac{2}{3}$.

Write this fraction $\frac{3}{5}$.

 (Hint) When there are three or more equal parts, fractions and ordinal numbers are alike. For example, three equal parts are called thirds. Six equal parts are called sixths. Ten equal parts are called tenths. The ordinal numbers for 3, 6, and 10 are third, sixth, and tenth.

Reading Fractions Practice

**Complete each fraction. Write the part that is shaded.
The first one has been done for you.**

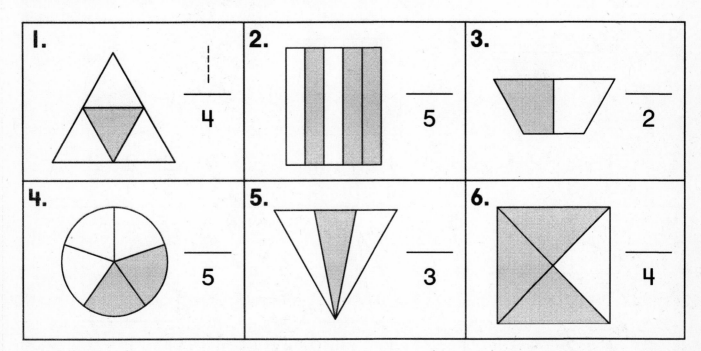

**Complete each fraction. Write the number of parts in all.
The first one has been done for you.**

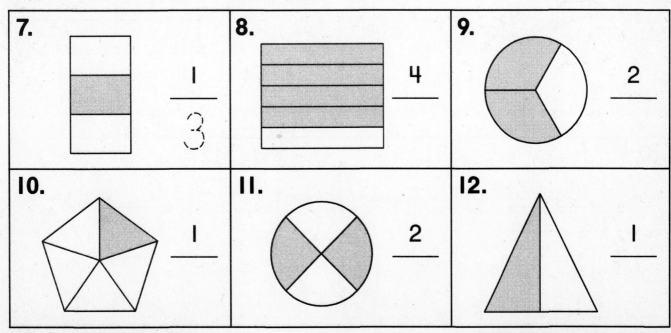

Reading Fractions More Practice

Ring the fraction that tells what part is shaded.
The first one has been done for you.

1. 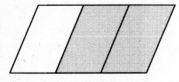 $\frac{1}{3}$ $\left(\frac{2}{3}\right)$ $\frac{2}{4}$	**2.** 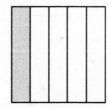 $\frac{1}{3}$ $\frac{1}{4}$ $\frac{1}{5}$	**3.** 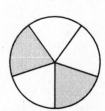 $\frac{2}{3}$ $\frac{2}{4}$ $\frac{2}{5}$
4. 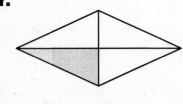 $\frac{1}{4}$ $\frac{2}{4}$ $\frac{3}{4}$	**5.** 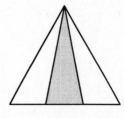 $\frac{1}{3}$ $\frac{1}{4}$ $\frac{2}{4}$	**6.**  $\frac{1}{4}$ $\frac{1}{2}$ $\frac{2}{4}$
7. 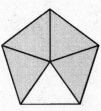 $\frac{1}{5}$ $\frac{2}{3}$ $\frac{4}{5}$	**8.** 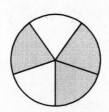 $\frac{3}{4}$ $\frac{3}{5}$ $\frac{4}{5}$	**9.** 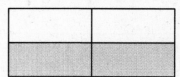 $\frac{1}{3}$ $\frac{2}{3}$ $\frac{2}{4}$
10. 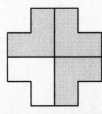 $\frac{3}{4}$ $\frac{2}{3}$ $\frac{2}{4}$	**11.**  $\frac{1}{4}$ $\frac{1}{5}$ $\frac{2}{5}$	**12.** 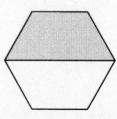 $\frac{1}{2}$ $\frac{1}{3}$ $\frac{1}{4}$

Geometry 1–2, SV 9781419099144

Reading Fractions Activities

Fraction Strips

Materials: Fraction Strips (page 120), glue, scissors, art paper

Steps to Follow:

1. Cut out each fraction strip.
2. Cut out the fraction pieces that name the fractions.
3. Match each fraction piece with the strip that it fits.
4. Glue the fraction strips onto art paper.
5. Glue one fraction piece on each fraction strip that it matches.

Color to Make Fractions

Materials: crayons

Steps to Follow:

1. Color each rectangle to show a different fraction.
2. Write the name of each fraction that you color.

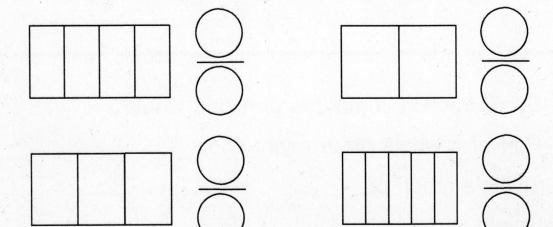

Unit 4: Equal Parts, Lesson 19
Geometry 1–2, SV 9781419099144

LESSON 20   Fractions in Groups

A fraction can name part of a group.

Look at the group of apples.
Count how many are shaded.
Count how many in all.

        | 1 apple is shaded.
---
5 apples in all.

$\frac{1}{5}$ of the group of apples is shaded.

What fraction is shown by the group of bananas?

   | 2 bananas are shaded.
---
3 bananas in all.

$\frac{2}{3}$ of the group of bananas is shaded.

 Every fraction compares part and whole.

Part of a whole pizza might show $\frac{1}{4}$.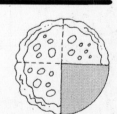

Part of a whole group of

oranges might show $\frac{1}{4}$.

Fractions in Groups Practice

Write each fraction to tell what part of the group is shaded. The first one has been done for you.

1. $\dfrac{3}{4}$	**2.** _____
3. _____	**4.** _____
5. _____	**6.** _____
7. _____	**8.** _____

Fractions in Groups More Practice

Color part of each group to show the fraction.
The first one has been done for you.

1.  $\dfrac{1}{2}$	**2.** 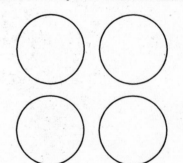 $\dfrac{2}{4}$
3. $\dfrac{3}{4}$	**4.** $\dfrac{1}{5}$
5. 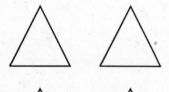 $\dfrac{1}{3}$	**6.**  $\dfrac{2}{3}$
7. 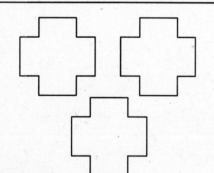 $\dfrac{2}{5}$	**8.** 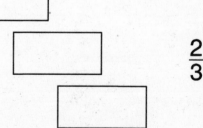 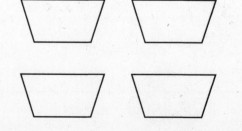 $\dfrac{1}{4}$

Fractions in Groups Activities

Fraction Matchups

Materials: Fraction Strips (page 120) and Fractions of Groups (page 121), scissors

Steps to Follow:

1. Cut out the fraction strips, fraction pieces, and fraction groups on pages 120 and 121.
2. Match fraction strips, fraction pieces, and fraction groups to show the same fractions.
3. Then mix up the pieces to play a game with a partner.
4. Each player needs a set of all the pieces.
5. Race to see who can match all of them first.

Make Fractions of Groups

Materials: index cards, two colors of counters

Steps to Follow:

1. Use ten index cards. Write a fraction on each card.

   $\frac{1}{2}$ $\frac{1}{3}$ $\frac{2}{3}$ $\frac{1}{4}$ $\frac{2}{4}$ $\frac{3}{4}$ $\frac{1}{5}$ $\frac{2}{5}$ $\frac{3}{5}$ $\frac{4}{5}$

2. Mix up the cards and then take one.
3. Use two colors of counters to show the fraction on the card.
4. Take turns with a partner until you have shown all of the fractions on the cards.

Assessment: Equal Parts

Ring the figure that shows a line of symmetry.

1.

2.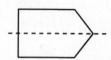

Ring the number of equal parts.

3.

0   4   5

4.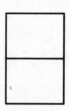

0   2   3

5.

0   3   4

Ring the fraction that tells what part is shaded.

6.

$\frac{1}{2}$ $\frac{1}{4}$ $\frac{1}{5}$

7.

$\frac{1}{3}$ $\frac{2}{3}$ $\frac{2}{4}$

8.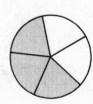

$\frac{2}{3}$ $\frac{2}{5}$ $\frac{3}{5}$

Write each fraction to tell what part of the group is shaded.

9.

10.

LESSON 21   Inches

An **inch** is a unit of measurement.

It is about the length of a small paper clip.

Look at the inch ruler below.

The paper clip and the ruler start along the same line.

The paper clip stops above the 1.

The paper clip is 1 inch long.

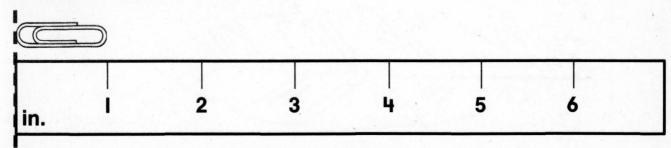

You can use inches to measure length.

Use an inch ruler to measure the pencil.

Place your ruler here. Be sure it starts at the dashed line.

The pencil is 5 inches long.

You can write 5 inches or 5 in. to tell the length.

 Hint You will get the right measure if the object and the ruler start at the same place.

Unit 5: Measurement, Lesson 21
Geometry 1–2, SV 9781419099144

Inches Practice

Use an inch ruler to measure each object.

1.

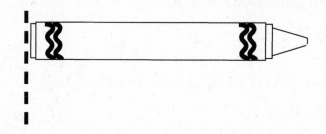

_____ inches

2.

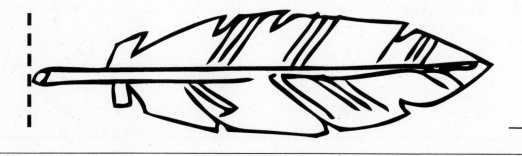

_____ inches

3.

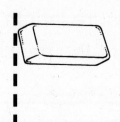

_____ inch

4.

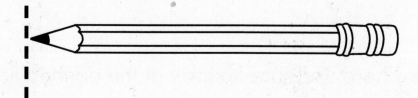

_____ inches

5.

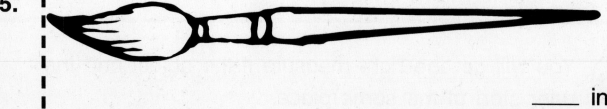

_____ inches

Inches More Practice

Use an inch ruler.
Ring the pencil in each pair that shows the correct measure.

1. 4 inches

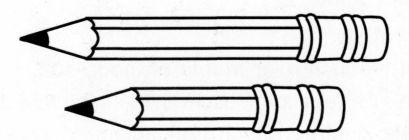

2. 2 inches

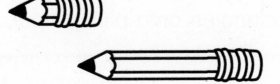

3. 6 inches

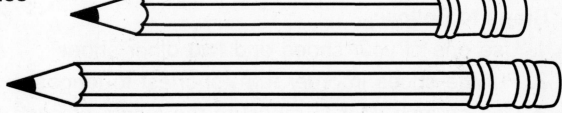

4. 3 inches

Unit 5: Measurement, Lesson 21
Geometry 1–2, SV 9781419099144

Inches Activities

How Long Is a Rectangle?

Materials: Inches (page 122), inch ruler, scissors, plain paper, paper strips

Steps to Follow:

1. Cut out the inch ruler that is on page 122.
2. Use the inch ruler to measure the length of each rectangle.
3. Write the length on each rectangle.
4. Cut more rectangles from art paper.
5. Write the length on each rectangle to the nearest inch.
6. Glue all of your rectangles onto plain paper.

Short, Medium, and Long Shoes

Materials: inch ruler, 3 shoes of different lengths, 3 sticky notes

Steps to Follow:

1. Use one of your shoes and two other shoes.
2. Put the shoes in order from shortest to longest.
3. Use an inch ruler to measure the length of each shoe.
4. Write the length of each shoe on a sticky note.
5. Put each sticky note on the wrong shoe.
6. Ask a partner to look at the shoes and put the correct note on each shoe.
7. Have your partner measure the shoes to check the answers.

Name _____ Date _____

LESSON 22　Centimeters

A **centimeter** is a unit of measurement.
It is about the length of a small button.

Look at the centimeter ruler below.
The button and the ruler start along the same line.
The button stops above the 1.
The button is 1 centimeter long.

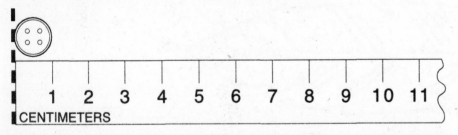

You can use centimeters to measure length.
Use a centimeter ruler to measure the scissors.

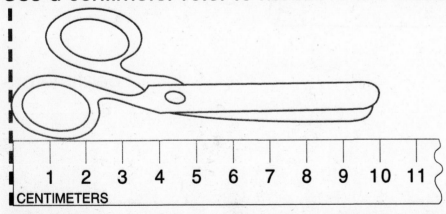

Place your ruler here. Be sure it starts at the dashed line.

The scissors are 10 centimeters long.
You can write 10 centimeters or 10 cm to tell the length.

 Hint Always line up the ruler and the object to start along the same line.

Unit 5: Measurement, Lesson 22
Geometry 1–2, SV 9781419099144

Centimeters Practice

Use a centimeter ruler to measure each object.

I.

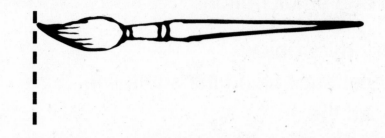

_____ centimeters

2.

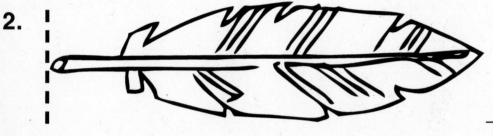

_____ centimeters

3.

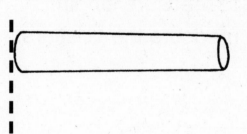

_____ centimeters

4.

_____ centimeters

5.

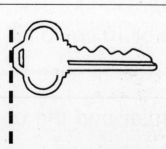

_____ centimeters

Unit 5: Measurement, Lesson 22
Geometry 1–2, SV 9781419099144

Centimeters More Practice

Use a centimeter ruler.
Ring the straw in each pair that shows the correct measure.

1. 8 centimeters

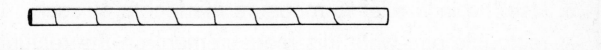

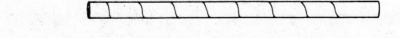

2. 3 centimeters

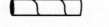

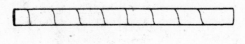

3. 6 centimeters

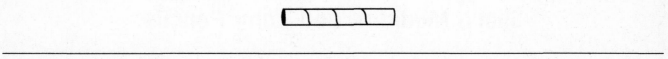

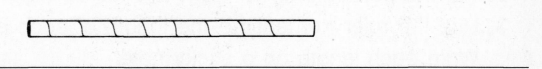

4. 11 centimeters

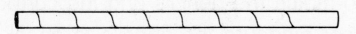

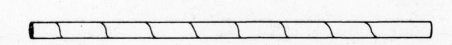

Centimeters Activities

How Long Is a Rectangle?

Materials: Centimeters (page 123), inch ruler, pencil

Steps to Follow:

1. Cut out the centimeter ruler that is on page 123.
2. Use the centimeter ruler to measure the length of each rectangle. Write the length on each rectangle.
3. Use the inch ruler to measure the length of each rectangle and write this measurement on the rectangle.
4. Are there more inches or centimeters in the two rectangles?

Short, Medium, and Long Pencils

Materials: centimeter ruler, 3 pencils, 3 sticky notes

Steps to Follow:

1. Use 3 pencils that are not the same length.
2. Put the pencils in order from shortest to longest.
3. Use the ruler to measure the length of each pencil. Write each length on a sticky note.
4. Put each sticky note on the wrong pencil.
5. Ask a partner to match the pencils and the correct notes.
6. Have your partner measure the pencils to check the answers.

LESSON 23   Perimeter

A farmer wanted to build a fence to keep his pigs in.
He measured around where the fence would go.
Then he knew how much fencing to buy.

The distance around a figure is
called the **perimeter**.
To find the perimeter, add the
length of each side.

The rectangle below is 3 inches
long and 2 inches wide.
Check these measures
with an inch ruler.

3 in.

2 in.   2 in.

3 in.

Add each side.

$$\underline{3} + \underline{2} + \underline{3} + \underline{2} = \underline{10} \text{ inches}$$

The perimeter of the rectangle is 10 inches.

(Hint) Make sure you add the length of each side. If there
are 4 sides, add 4 lengths to find the perimeter.

Perimeter Practice

Use an inch ruler to measure each side.
Find the perimeter of each figure.

I.

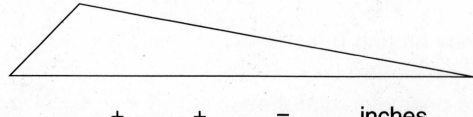

_____ + _____ + _____ = _____ inches

2.

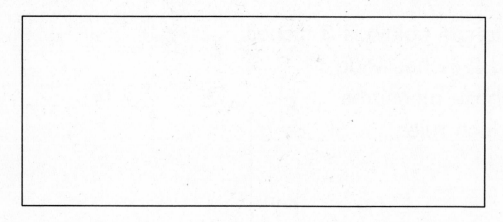

_____ + _____ + _____ + _____ = _____ inches

3.

_____ + _____ + _____ + _____ = _____ inches

Perimeter More Practice

Use a centimeter ruler to measure each side.
Find the perimeter of each figure.

1.

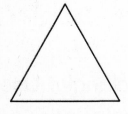

_____ + _____ + _____ = _____ cm

2.

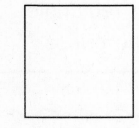

_____ + _____ + _____ + _____ = _____ cm

3.

_____ + _____ + _____ + _____ = _____ cm

4.

_____ + _____ + _____ + _____ = _____ cm

Unit 5: Measurement, Lesson 23
Geometry 1–2, SV 9781419099144

Perimeter Activities

Cut and Measure Perimeter of Shapes

Materials: Inches (page 122), Centimeters (page 123), scissors, art paper

Steps to Follow:

1. Cut out a rectangle from art paper.
2. Measure to find the perimeter of your rectangle. Use the inch ruler on page 122 or the centimeter ruler on page 123.
3. Ask a friend to guess the perimeter of your rectangle.
4. Then have your friend measure to check the guess.

Find the Perimeter of Classroom Objects

Materials: inch ruler, book, flat eraser, calculator

Steps to Follow:

1. Get any book, any size flat eraser, and a calculator.
2. Measure each side of the objects to find the perimeter.
3. Write each measure to the nearest inch.
4. Add all four sides of each object.
5. Use the calculator to add the sides if you need to.
6. Tell a friend one of the perimeters you found.
7. Ask your friend to guess which object matches that perimeter.
8. Have your friend measure to check the guess.

LESSON 24   Area

How many square stones does it take
to make a walkway?
The walkway below uses 2 rows of stones.
There are 10 stones in each row.

Count the square stones in the walkway.
There are 20 square stones in all.

The number of squares inside a shape is called the **area**.
To find the area, count the squares that fill the shape.

The rectangle below is 5 squares long.
There are 3 rows of squares.

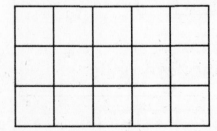

There are 15 squares inside the rectangle.
The area of the rectangle is 15 square units.

 Hint   A figure has area even if it is not a rectangle. You can
count or estimate the number of square units inside.

105

Name _____ Date _____

Area Practice

Find the area of each figure.

1.

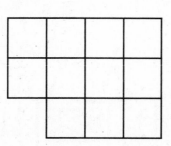

_____ square units

2.

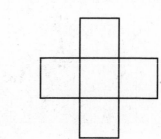

_____ square units

3.

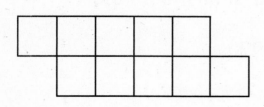

_____ square units

4.

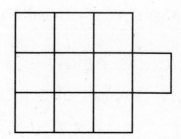

_____ square units

5.

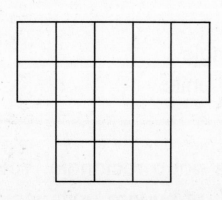

_____ square units

6.

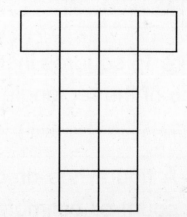

_____ square units

Unit 5: Measurement, Lesson 24
Geometry 1–2, SV 9781419099144

Name _____ Date _____

Area More Practice

Find the area of each rectangle.

1.

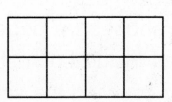

_____ square units

2.

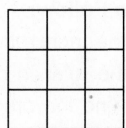

_____ square units

3.

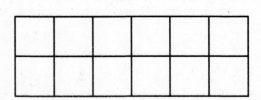

_____ square units

4.

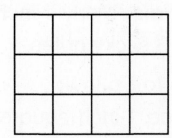

_____ square units

5.

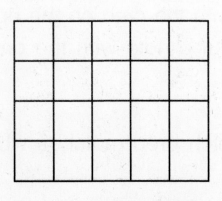

_____ square units

6.

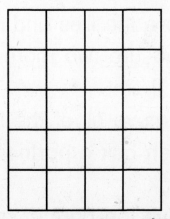

_____ square units

Unit 5: Measurement, Lesson 24
Geometry 1–2, SV 9781419099144

Name _____ Date _____

Area Activities

Measure Area of Shapes

Materials: Inches (page 122), scissors

Steps to Follow:

1. Use the inch ruler to measure the shapes on page 122.
2. Use the ruler to draw 1-inch squares inside each shape.
3. Then find the area of the shapes by counting the squares.

Use Tiles to Find Area

Materials: many 1-inch tiles, 3 books that are different sizes, 3 sticky notes

Steps to Follow:

1. Place 1-inch square tiles on top of a book to cover it as much as you can.
2. Count the number of square tiles that you use.
3. Write the area on a sticky note.
4. Move the tiles and put the note with the area on the book.
5. Measure two more books and put a note with the area on them.
6. Remove all of the sticky notes.
7. Then ask a partner to guess which area matches which book.
8. Have the partner use square tiles to check each guess.

Name _____ Date _____

LESSON 25   Perimeter and Area

You can use grid paper to find perimeter and area.
Count units around the outside to find perimeter.
Count square units inside to find area.

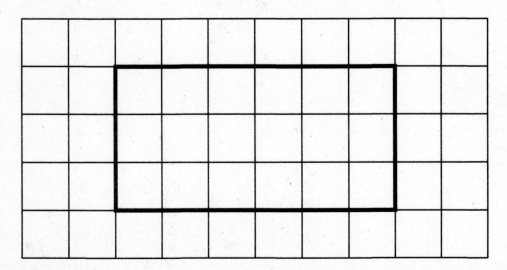

The rectangle is 6 units long and 3 units wide.
Add the sides to find perimeter.

$$\underline{6} + \underline{3} + \underline{6} + \underline{3} = \underline{18} \text{ units}$$

Count the squares inside to find area.
There are 18 squares inside the rectangle.

The area of the rectangle is $\underline{18}$ square units.

 Hint The perimeter of a figure is the same no matter how
you turn it. This is also true for the area.

Perimeter and Area Practice

Find the perimeter and area for each rectangle.

1.

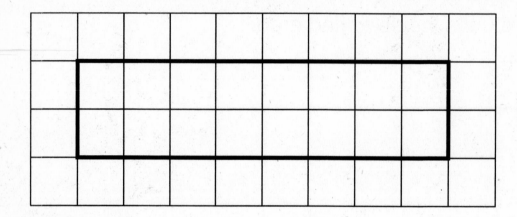

Perimeter ____ + ____ + ____ + ____ = ____ units

Area ____ square units

2.

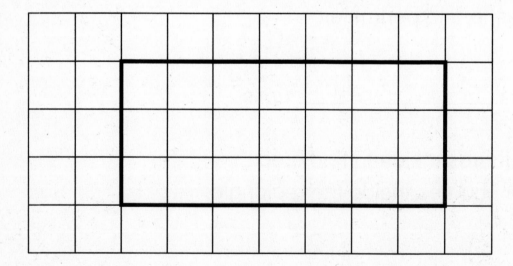

Perimeter ____ + ____ + ____ + ____ = ____ units

Area ____ square units

www.harcourtschoolsupply.com
110
Unit 5: Measurement, Lesson 25
Geometry 1-2, SV 9781419099144

Name _____ Date _____

Perimeter and Area More Practice

Find the perimeter and area for each figure.

1.

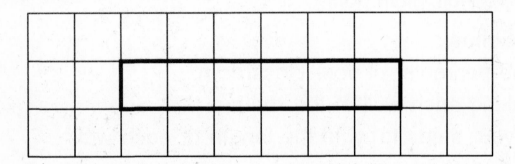

Perimeter   ____ + ____ + ____ + ____ = ____ units

Area   ____ square units

2.

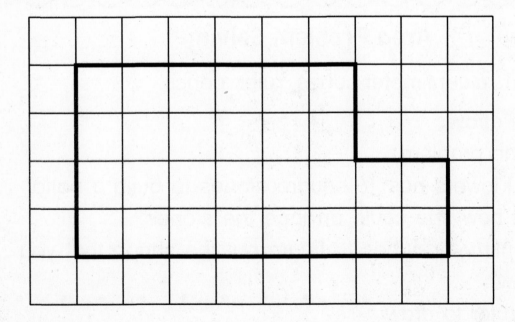

Perimeter   ____ + ____ + ____ + ____ + ____ + ____

= ____ units

Area   ____ square units

111

Perimeter and Area Activities

Perimeter Walkabout

Materials: pencil, plain paper

Steps to Follow:

1. Find the perimeter of your classroom.
2. Walk along each wall of the room.
3. Count your steps to write the length of each wall.
4. Add your steps to find the perimeter.
5. Some people will have a different answer. Discuss why.
6. Now go on a perimeter walkabout around another room.

Area Problem Solving

Materials: 16 centimeter cubes, ruler, pencil

Steps to Follow:

1. Read the problem.

   Miss Flowers has 16 square stones to build a patio.
   Show how she could arrange the stones.

2. Use centimeter cubes to figure out the shape that you will draw.

3. Use a ruler to draw the shape on the dot paper at right.

Assessment: Measurement

Use an inch ruler to measure each crayon.

1.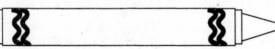

____ inches

2.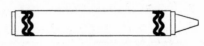

____ inches

Use a centimeter ruler to measure each stick.

3.

____ centimeters

4.

____ centimeters

Find the perimeter and area for each rectangle.

5.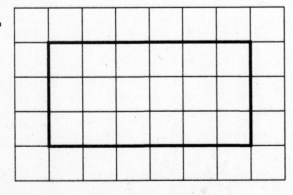

Perimeter = ____ units

Area = ____ square units

6.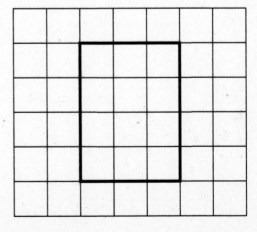

Perimeter = ____ units

Area = ____ square units

Sorting Chart

Flat Shapes

Activity Master 2

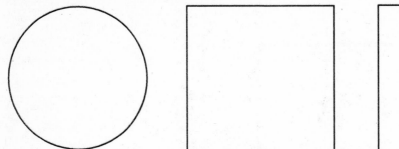

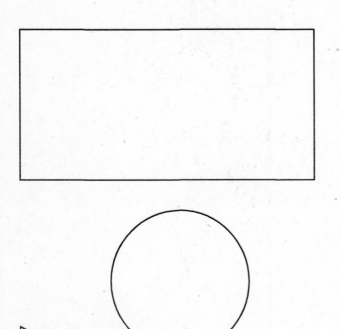

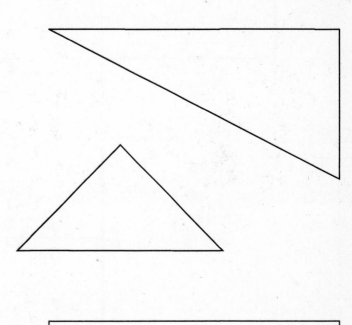

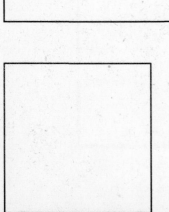

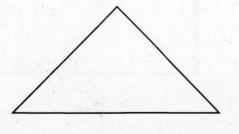

Blackline Masters
Geometry 1–2, SV 978141909144

Cube Net

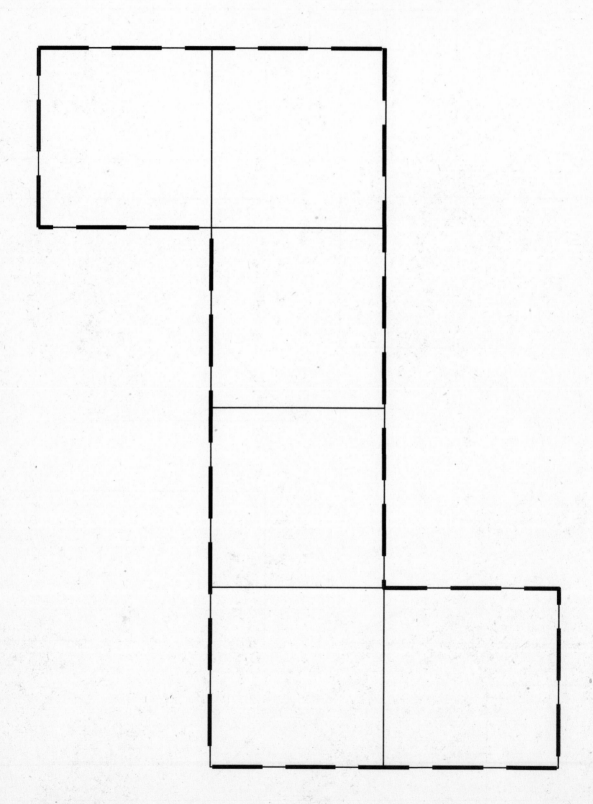

Solid Shapes

 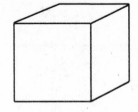 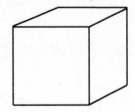 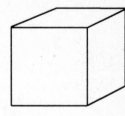

 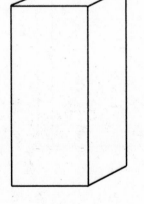 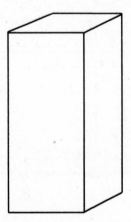 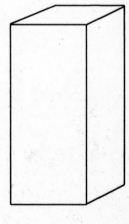

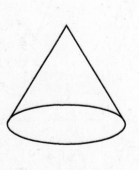

  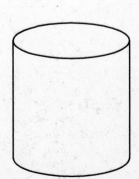

A Place for Everything

Activity Master 5

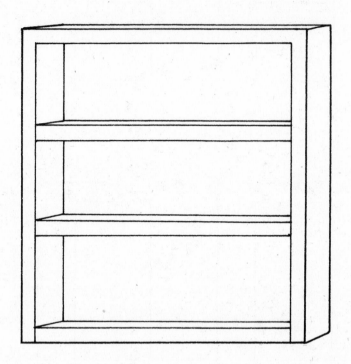

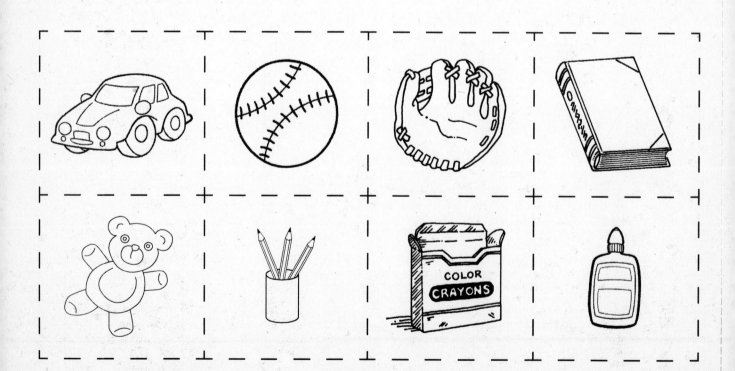

Park Map

4

3

2

1

0   1   2   3   4

Name ______________________________ Date ______________

Fraction Strips

Activity Master 7

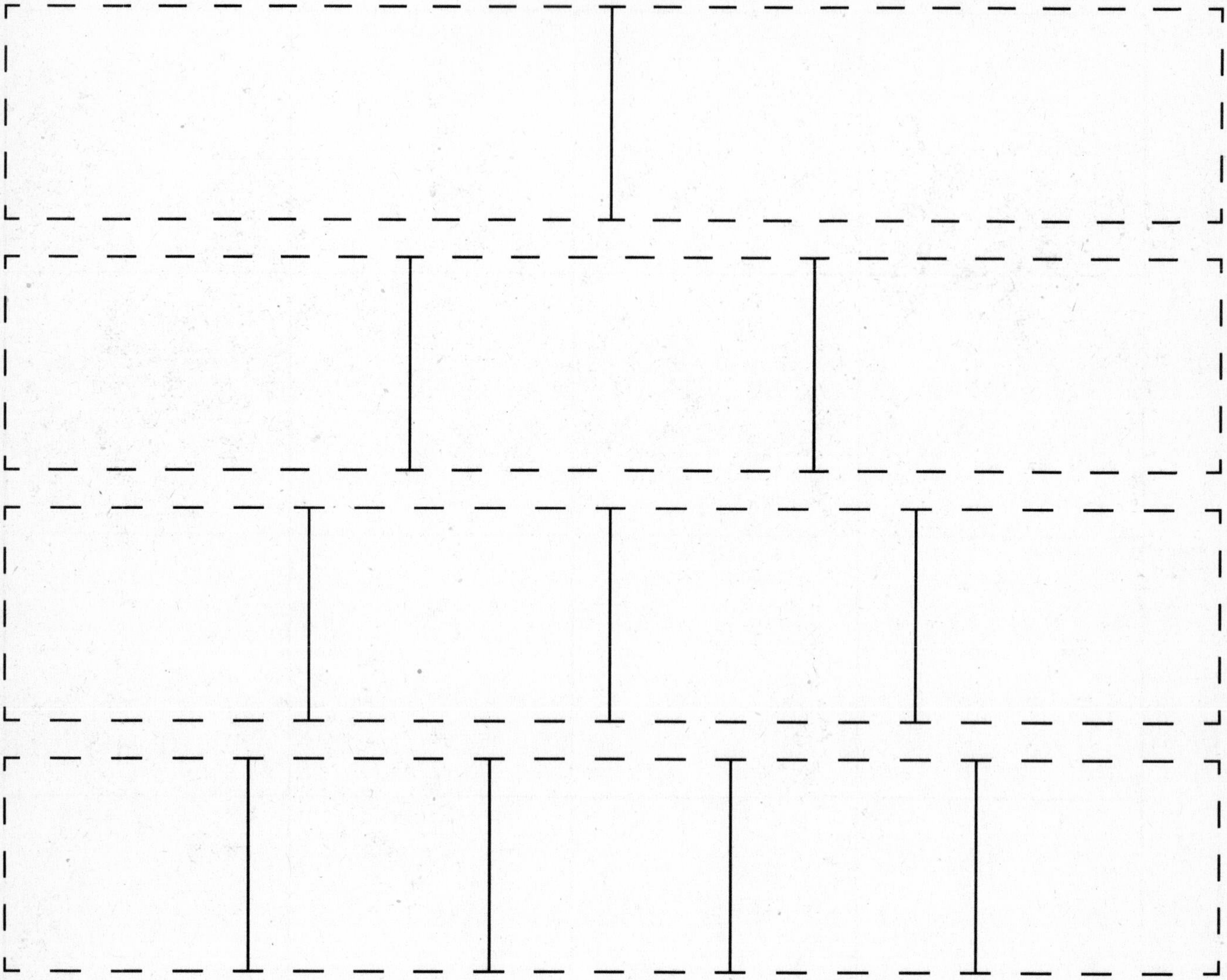

one half $\frac{1}{2}$

one third $\frac{1}{3}$

one fourth $\frac{1}{4}$

one fifth $\frac{1}{5}$

Name _____   Date _____

Fractions of Groups

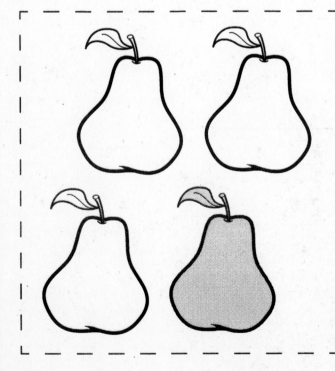

Blackline Masters
Geometry 1–2, SV 9781419099144

Inches

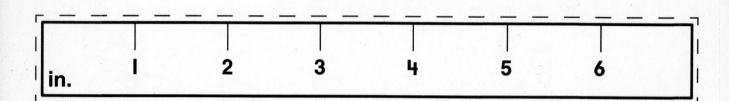

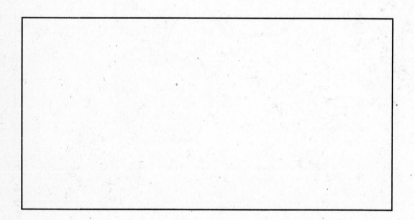

Centimeters

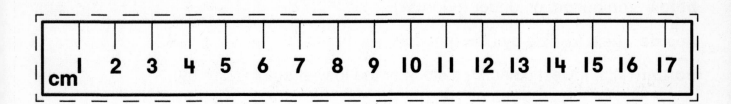

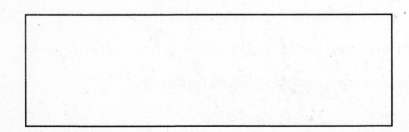

Glossary

above   on top of, over (page 59)

area   the number of square units inside a flat figure or space (page 105)

below   on bottom of, under (page 59)

beside   next to, side by side (page 59)

bottom   the lowest object in a stack or the lowest point (page 59)

centimeter   a unit to measure length that is about as wide as a little finger (page 97)

circle   a round flat shape that is the same all around (page 21)

closed figure   a figure that begins and ends at the same point (page 9)

cone   a solid figure with a circle at one end and a point at the other end (page 38)

congruent   two figures that are the same size and shape (page 25)

corner   the point where two lines meet (pages 13 and 42)

cube   a box with 6 sides having squares as faces (page 34)

cylinder   a can having a circle at both ends (page 38)

edge   the straight lines that make each face on a solid figure (page 34)

face   each flat surface on a solid figure (page 34)

fifths   five equal parts of a whole figure or a whole group (page 80)

flip   to move a shape across a line to make a mirror image (page 51)

footprint   a mark left by pressing or stamping a shape on a flat surface (page 30)

fourths   four equal parts of a whole figure or a whole group (page 80)

fraction   a relationship that compares parts and the total number of equal parts (page 84)

graph   a grid or map with evenly spaced rows and columns to show specific points (page 67)

halves   two equal parts of a whole figure or a whole group (page 76)

inch   a unit to measure length that is about as long as a small paper clip (page 93)

line   a straight edge with arrows at both ends to show that it never ends (page 63)

line of symmetry   a line that divides a figure into two equal parts that are mirror images (page 72)

line segment   a straight edge with points at both ends to show where it ends (page 63)

middle   in the center (page 59)

number line   a line with points labeled as numbers to show specific positions (page 63)

one fifth   one part out of five equal parts (page 80)

one fourth   one part out of four equal parts (page 80)

one half   one part out of two equal parts (page 76)

one third   one part out of three equal parts (page 76)

open figure   a figure that does not begin and end at the same point (page 9)

pattern   an order that repeats in a way that you can guess what comes next (page 46)

perimeter   the distance around a figure, or the sum of all the sides (page 101)

point   a mark to show a specific place on a line or to show where a line segment ends (page 63)

rectangle   a flat shape with 4 sides, 4 square corners, and opposite sides of the same length (page 17)

rectangular prism   a box with 6 sides having rectangles as faces (page 34)

side   a straight edge of a flat shape (page 13)

slide   to move a shape along a straight path without turning (page 51)

sphere   a ball that is the same size all around (page 34)

square   a flat shape with 4 sides that are the same length and 4 corners that are the same size (page 17)

square corner   where two lines cross at 90°, like a plus sign (page 17)

thirds   three equal parts of a whole figure or a whole group (page 76)

top   the highest object in a stack or the highest point (page 59)

triangle   a flat shape with 3 sides and 3 corners (page 21)

turn   to move a shape around a point, to rotate (page 51)

Answer Key

Level Assessment

Page 5
1. Ring second and third figures.
2. The square has 4 sides and 4 corners. The triangle has 3 sides and 3 corners.
3. Color the circle red, the square blue, the rectangle green, and the triangle yellow.
4. Color 2 cubes blue, 2 cylinders red, and 2 rectangular prisms yellow.

Page 6
5. square
6. flip
7. turn
8. Color middle cylinder.
9. Color top block.
10. Mark a red dot at coordinates (2, 2).
11. Mark a blue dot at coordinates (5, 3).

Page 7
12. Ring second figure.
13. Ring first figure.
14. 5
15. 2
16. 4
17. $\frac{1}{5}$
18. $\frac{2}{3}$
19. $\frac{1}{4}$
20. $\frac{1}{3}$
21. $\frac{3}{5}$

Page 8
22. 1 inch
23. 3 inches
24. 6 centimeters
25. 3 centimeters
26. P = 16 units, A = 15 square units
27. P = 16 units, A = 16 square units

Unit 1: Plane Figures

Page 10
1. Ring first and third figures.
2. Ring third and fourth figures.
3. Ring first, third, and fourth figures.
4. Ring third figure.

Page 11
1. Color second and third figures.
2. Color first and second figures.
3. Color second and third figures.
4. Draw any closed figure.
5. Draw any open figure.

Page 12
1. Completed charts show that O, B, and D are closed and C, M, and L are open.
2. Make one chain of loops that holds together and one chain of pipe cleaners that does not hold together.

Page 14
1. Draw a dot on each corner. The circles have no dots.
2. Trace each straight side red. The circle and oval will not have any tracing.

Page 15
1. 3 sides, 3 corners
2. 4 sides, 4 corners
3. 3 sides, 3 corners
4. 6 sides, 6 corners
5. 4 sides, 4 corners
6. 4 sides, 4 corners

Page 16
1. Draw and color a square and write 4.
2. Draw any polygon and describe it to another child.

Page 18
1. Ring first and fourth shapes.
2. Ring second and third shapes.
3. Ring second and fourth shapes.
4. Ring first and second shapes.

Page 19
Color the 4 squares red and the 5 rectangles blue.

Page 20
1. Explore to find that a square will fold into a triangle but a rectangle will not.

2. Sort shapes to find those with 4 corners and trace a square or rectangle and a rhombus or trapezoid.

Page 22
1. Ring the first and fourth shapes.
2. Ring the second and fourth shapes.
3. Ring the second and fourth shapes.
4. Ring the first and fourth shapes.

Page 23
Color the 5 triangles red and the 4 circles blue.

Page 24
1. Make a mask using triangles and circles.
2. Completed charts show triangles in column labeled 3 and squares and rectangles in column labeled 4.

Page 26
1. Color second and fourth shapes.
2. Color first and fourth shapes.
3. Color second and third shapes.
4. Color first and third shapes.

Page 27
1. Draw a triangle that is congruent to the one given.
2. Draw a rectangle that is congruent to the one given.
3. Draw a square that is congruent to the one given.
4. Draw a triangle that is congruent to the one given.

Page 28
1. Draw, cut out, and match three pairs of congruent shapes.
2. Make leaf rubbings and compare them to the leaves used.

Page 29
1. Ring second and fourth figures.
2. 3 sides and corners, 4 sides and corners

3. Color 2 circles red, 1 square blue, 3 rectangles green, and 3 triangles yellow.
4. Draw a triangle that is congruent to the one given.

Unit 2: Solid Figures

Page 31
1. Ring the circle that is in the middle.
2. Ring the rectangle.
3. Ring the circle.
4. Ring the square.
5. Ring the triangle.

Page 32
1. d
2. a
3. c
4. b
5. 2
6. 1

Page 33
1. Make footprints of 3 or 4 blocks and match blocks and footprints.
2. Trace the footprints of 2 blocks and match blocks and footprints.

Page 35
1. Color 3 cubes green.
2. Color 4 rectangular prisms that are not cubes purple.
3. Color 5 spheres yellow.

Page 36
1. cube
2. sphere
3. rectangular prism
4. rectangular prism

Page 37
1. Make a cube from a net.
2. Completed charts will show labels *BOXES* and *BALLS* and will have marks to show how many of each.

Page 39
1. Color 5 cylinders blue.
2. Color 5 cones orange.
3. Draw an *X* on 2 cubes.

Geometry 1–2, SV 9781419099144

Page 40
1. cylinder
2. cone
3. sphere
4. cylinder

Page 41
1. Make a cylinder.
2. Describe solid shapes by whether they roll.

Page 43
1. Color 2 cubes and 3 rectangular prisms.
2. Ring 2 cylinders and 1 cone.
3. Write *X* on 4 spheres.

Page 44
1. megaphone
2. tissue box
3. can
4. ball
5. rectangular box

Page 45
1. Completed building and image on art paper should match.
2. Describe solid shapes by their faces, edges, and corners.

Page 47
1. rectangular prism
2. cylinder
3. rectangular prism
4. cone

Page 48
1. triangle
2. rectangle
3. triangle
4. rectangle
5. taller triangle

Page 49
1. Create a predictable pattern using circles and triangles.
2. Create a predictable block pattern and identify missing pieces of a pattern.

Page 50
1. circle
2. Color 2 cubes blue and write *X* on 2 cylinders.
3. triangle
4. rectangle

Unit 3: Movement and Location
Page 52
1. turn
2. flip
3. turn
4. slide

Page 53
1. Draw a congruent triangle in the same orientation as the first.
2. Draw a mirror image of the shape.
3. Draw a rotation of the arrow to point a different direction.

Page 54
1. Demonstrate slides, flips, and turns on geoboards.
2. Demonstrate slides, flips, and turns.

Page 56
1. Ring the triangle.
2. Ring the stacked boxes.
3. Ring the parallelogram.

Page 57
1. Answers will vary. One possible answer is rectangle that is 4 squares by 2 squares.
2. Answers will vary. One possible answer is rectangle that is 3 squares by 2 squares.
3. Answers will vary. One possible answer is 3 by 3 square.

Page 58
1. Trace 8 squares: 6 smaller squares and 2 larger squares.
   Trace 12 triangles: 8 smaller triangles and 4 larger triangles.
2. Designs and shapes will vary.

Page 60
1. Color the bottom block.
2. Color the middle block.
3. Color the middle block.
4. Color the top block.

Page 61
1.–2. Completed grid will show a circle in the top left box and a square in the bottom right box.

3.–4. Completed grid will show a triangle in the bottom left box and a circle in the bottom middle box.
5.–6. Completed grid will show an *X* in the top right box and a *Z* in the bottom middle box.
7.–8. Completed grid will show an *S* in the top middle box and a *W* in the bottom middle box.

Page 62
1. Tell the position of each item on the completed bookshelf.
2. Demonstrate an understanding of position words while playing a game.

Page 64
1. Ring the second figure.
2. Ring the first figure.
3. 2
4. 6
5. 1

Page 65
1. Color house 4.
2. Color house 5.
3. Color house 3.
4. Color house 6.

Page 66
1. Make a floor number line and give directions.
2. Make a row of houses and give directions.

Page 68
1. Mark a blue dot at coordinates (3, 4).
2. Mark a red dot at coordinates (1, 6).
3. Mark a black dot at coordinates (6, 1).
4. Mark a yellow dot at coordinates (4, 3).
5. Mark a green dot at coordinates (5, 2).
6. Mark a brown dot at coordinates (2, 5).

Page 69
1. pig race
2. popcorn
3. games
4. circus tent

Page 70
1. Create matching maps.
2. Play a game on a grid.

Page 71
1. flip
2. slide
3. Ring the rectangle in the middle.
4. Color the middle block.
5. Color the top block.
6. Mark a red dot at coordinates (3, 2).
7. Mark a blue dot at coordinates (6, 4).

Unit 4: Equal Parts
Page 73
1. Ring the first figure.
2. Ring the second figure.
3. Ring the second figure.
4. Ring the first figure.
5. Ring the first figure.
6. Ring the first figure.
7. Ring the second figure.
8. Ring the first figure.

Page 74
1. horizontal line of symmetry
2. vertical line of symmetry
3. vertical line of symmetry
4. vertical line of symmetry
5. horizontal or vertical line of symmetry
6. vertical line of symmetry
7. vertical line of symmetry
8. vertical line of symmetry
9. vertical line of symmetry
10. horizontal or vertical lines of symmetry; diagonal lines also possible
11. horizontal or vertical lines of symmetry
12. horizontal or vertical lines of symmetry; diagonal lines also possible

Page 75
1. Fold and cut shapes to show a line of symmetry.
2. Use a fold to create a mirror image.

Page 77
1. 2
2. 0
3. 3
4. 2
5. 2
6. 3
7. 0
8. 2
9. 3
10. 2
11. 3
12. 0

Geometry 1–2, SV 9781419099144

Page 78
1. Color the third figure.
2. Color the first figure.
3. Color the first figure.
4. Color the second figure.

Page 79
1. Folded squares will demonstrate horizontal, vertical, and diagonal halves.
2. Folded squares will demonstrate horizontal and vertical thirds.

Page 81
1. 5
2. 4
3. 0
4. 4
5. 0
6. 5
7. 5
8. 0
9. 4
10. 4
11. 0
12. 5

Page 82
1. Color the first figure.
2. Color the third figure.
3. Color the first figure.
4. Color the second figure.

Page 83
1. Fold and decorate paper to show equal fourths.
2. Play a game to fill five fifths of a fraction strip.

Page 85
1. 1
2. 3
3. 1
4. 2
5. 1
6. 3
7. 3
8. 5
9. 3
10. 5
11. 4
12. 2

Page 86
1. $\frac{2}{3}$
2. $\frac{1}{5}$
3. $\frac{2}{5}$
4. $\frac{1}{4}$
5. $\frac{1}{3}$
6. $\frac{1}{2}$

7. $\frac{4}{5}$
8. $\frac{3}{5}$
9. $\frac{2}{4}$
10. $\frac{3}{4}$
11. $\frac{1}{5}$
12. $\frac{1}{2}$

Page 87
1. Match fraction strips and names of fractions.
2. Numerators will vary. Denominators are 4, 2, 3, and 5.

Page 89
1. $\frac{3}{4}$
2. $\frac{1}{2}$
3. $\frac{1}{3}$
4. $\frac{2}{5}$
5. $\frac{4}{5}$
6. $\frac{1}{4}$
7. $\frac{2}{3}$
8. $\frac{3}{5}$

Page 90
1. Color 1 square.
2. Color 2 circles.
3. Color 3 triangles.
4. Color 1 star.
5. Color 1 cross.
6. Color 2 rectangles.
7. Color 2 ovals.
8. Color 1 trapezoid.

Page 91
1. Match fraction strips, fraction pieces, and fractions of groups.
2. Create fraction groups to match fractions.

Page 92
1. Ring the first figure.
2. Ring the second figure.
3. 0
4. 2
5. 4
6. $\frac{1}{4}$
7. $\frac{1}{3}$
8. $\frac{3}{5}$
9. $\frac{3}{4}$
10. $\frac{1}{2}$

Unit 5: Measurement
Page 94
1. 3 inches
2. 5 inches
3. 1 inch
4. 4 inches
5. 6 inches

Page 95
1. Ring the first pencil.
2. Ring the second pencil.
3. Ring the second pencil.
4. Ring the second pencil.

Page 96
1. Rectangles are 4 inches long and 5 inches long. Answer will vary on other rectangles that children create.
2. Measure shoes and match notes showing each length.

Page 98
1. 9 cm
2. 12 cm
3. 6 cm
4. 2 cm
5. 4 cm

Page 99
1. Ring the first straw.
2. Ring the second straw.
3. Ring the first straw.
4. Ring the second straw.

Page 100
1. Rectangles are 10 cm long and 6 cm long. Rectangles are $3\frac{15}{16}$ inches and $2\frac{5}{16}$ inches long. There are more centimeters in the rectangles.
2. Arrange pencils from shortest to longest and measure the pencils.

Page 102
1. 5 + 1 + 4 = 10 inches
2. 5 + 2 + 5 + 2 = 14 inches
3. 2 + 2 + 2 + 2 = 8 inches

Page 103
1. 3 + 3 + 3 = 9 cm
2. 3 + 3 + 3 + 3 = 12 cm
3. 10 + 2 + 10 + 2 = 24 cm
4. 9 + 1 + 9 + 1 = 20 cm

Page 104
1. Perimeters of created rectangles will vary.
2. Measure classroom objects to find and compare perimeters.

Page 106
1. 11 square units
2. 5 square units
3. 10 square units
4. 10 square units
5. 16 square units
6. 12 square units

Page 107
1. 8 square units
2. 9 square units
3. 12 square units
4. 12 square units
5. 20 square units
6. 20 square units

Page 108
1. Rectangles from page 122 have areas of 8 square inches and 5 square inches.
2. Measure and estimate area using square tiles.

Page 110
1. 8 + 2 + 8 + 2 = 20 units; 16 square units
2. 7 + 3 + 7 + 3 = 20 units; 21 square units

Page 111
1. 6 + 1 + 6 + 1 = 14 units; 6 square units
2. 6 + 2 + 2 + 2 + 8 + 4 = 24 units; 28 square units

Page 112
1. Measure perimeter by the number of steps they take.
2. Answers will vary. If children draw rectangles, the possible answers are 6 by 2 and 4 by 4.

Page 113
1. 3 inches
2. 2 inches
3. 7 cm
4. 4 cm
5. 18 units, 18 square units
6. 14 units, 12 square units